Kundalini Yoga for Evolving People

Empowering Yourself in a World of Constant Change

—

BY MUTSHAT SHEMSUT-GIANPREM KAUR

A KUNDALINI RESEARCH INSTITUTE PUBLICATION

KRI PUBLICATIONS

© 2023 KUNDALINI RESEARCH INSTITUTE (2nd Edition)

BY MUTSHAT SHEMSUT-GIANPREM KAUR (ROBYN MAHONE-LONESOME)

PUBLISHED BY THE KUNDALINI RESEARCH INSTITUTE

TRAINING • PUBLISHING • RESEARCH • RESOURCES

PO BOX 1819 / SANTA CRUZ, NM 87532

WWW.KUNDALINIRESEARCHINSTITUTE.ORG

ISBN: 978-0-9786989-4-2

MANAGING EDITOR: MARIANA LAGE (HARISHABAD KAUR)

CONSULTING EDITOR: AMRIT SINGH KHALSA

COVER AND CREATIVE CONCEPT: FERNANDA MONTE-MÓR

REVIEW: SIRI NEEL KAUR KHALSA AND DIANA NANU

PROOFREADING: CARLOS ANDREI SIQUARA

LAYOUT: CAROLINE GISCHEWSKI

PHOTOGRAPHY: COCHE PRODUCTIONS™ PHOTO STUDIO

MODELS: FADJA ROBERT-CARR, KASHON DUBOSE AND MUTSHAT SHEMSUT-GIANPREM KAUR

EDITORIAL ASSISTANT: ANTONIO LARA SILVA

The diet, exercise and lifestyle suggestions in this book come from ancient yogic traditions. Nothing in this book should be construed as medical advice. Neither the author nor the publisher shall be liable or responsible for any loss, injury, damage, allegedly arising from any information or suggestion in this book. The benefits attributed to the practice of Kundalini Yoga and meditation stem from centuries-old yogic tradition. Results will vary with individuals. Always check with your personal physician or licensed care practitioner before making any significant modification in your diet or lifestyle, to ensure that the lifestyle changes are appropriate for your personal health condition and consistent with any medication you may be taking.

This publication has received the KRI Seal of Approval. This Seal is given only to products that have been reviewed for accuracy and integrity of the sections containing the 3HO lifestyle and Kundalini Yoga as taught by Yogi Bhajan®. For more information about Kundalini Yoga as taught by Yogi Bhajan® please see **www.kundaliniresearchinstitute.org.**

In memory of my father, Robert Lee Mahone,
Great-Grandmother Mary Jane Clark Simmons,
Malidoma Patrice Some, Baba, medicine man,
divine healer, author and teacher
and Stephanie Alston- Nero, artist-poet-healer-educator.

A woman's heart should be so hidden in God
that a man has to seek Him just to find her.
Maya Angelou

Healing comes when the individual remembers his or her
identity — the purpose chosen in the world of ancestral wisdom
— and reconnects with that world of spirit. Human beings long
for connection, and our sense of usefulness derives from the
feeling of connectedness. When we are connected — to our own
purpose, to the community around us, and to our spiritual wisdom
— we are able to live and act with authentic effectiveness.[1]
Malidoma Patrice Somé

Kundalini Yoga is like a sun – it serves all without discrimination.[2]
Yogi Bhajan

1   Somé, Malidoma Patrice. The Healing Wisdom of Africa: Finding Life Purpose Through
Nature, Ritual, and Community. Tarcher, 1999, p. 35-36.

2   The Library of Teachings, March 23, 1990.

FOREWORD

The first time I read *The Bluest Eye* by Tony Morrison, I realized that she had written this book for girls like me. The book inspired me, and I began to understand more about myself as a little Black girl and my place in the world. Every once in a while, a teacher or a writer comes along and creates social change by sharing their experience and knowledge. *Kundalini Yoga for Evolving People*, by MutShat Shemsut-Gianprem Kaur, is such a book.

This book was created to motivate everyone, and particularly people of color, to realize the benefits of the ancient practice of Kundalini Yoga and meditation, which has transformed lives for millennia. Kundalini Yoga and meditation were first acknowledged in the sacred Vedic teachings of the Upanishads (c. 1,000 B.C. - 500 B.C.) and were taught only in India until they were introduced to the West by Yogi Bhajan in 1968.

Through the practice of meditation and yoga, many will find ways to deal with the everyday conundrums and challenges of life. *Kundalini Yoga for Evolving People* presents Kundalini Yoga meditation as an ancient practice from which all can derive contemporary benefit. MutShat Shemsut-Gianprem Kaur has created this book as a guide to support the study of meditation as a practice. Kundalini Yoga meditation teaches one to slow down and take time to be with one-self; connect to the breath; go within; calm the mind; renew strength; and invigorate one's well-being. This book is also a tool for creating a personal revolution of health, wellness, and social change.

An area of focus within this book, titled "A Special Note to Black People of the Diaspora", speaks to the violence that impacts people of color, the microaggressions that are faced in work environments, and the challenges of "an uneven playing field." We are encouraged to practice Sankofa, a powerful Ghanaian word that is translated as "Go back and get it." In order for people to survive and thrive today, we must "go back and get it." We can do this through the practice of Kundalini Yoga and meditation.

The knowledge and practice of Kundalini Yoga and meditation as suggested by MutShat Shemsut-Gianprem Kaur here clearly shows the reader that it is possible to achieve "spiritual health, happiness, and abundance".

Maya Breuer
E-RYT 500, YACEP
President Emeritus Black Yoga Teachers Alliance,
Emeritus Trustee, Kripalu Center for Yoga and Health

TABLE OF CONTENTS

—

WORKING ON THE SPIRITUAL 72

DEVELOPING NEW HABITS 100

INTRODUCTION

—

I practice and teach Kundalini Yoga because it works. It is because it worked so well for me that I came up with the idea for this book: a collection of some of the most valuable techniques I have used to uplift, sustain, and improve myself over the past 20 years. This sacred science can work for you too.

These Kundalini Yoga meditations are part of an inspiring spiritual system that can help expand your awareness and instill a general sense of well-being. Kundalini Yoga as taught by Yogi Bhajan® is a mind-body science that raises the spirit—the part of ourselves that communicates with God, the universe, infinity, and the unknown. Because the spirit is unlimited, it does not discriminate. As a result, Kundalini Yoga is for everyone—each and every one of us. It is non-denominational and universal.

My focus in Kundalini Yoga studies has always been not only on the teachings but also on whether or not they resonated with my soul, that immortal part of myself. If, after reading this book and practicing the meditations, you decide to seek out a Kundalini Yoga studio, remember that the teachings of Kundalini Yoga go beyond the teacher who sits in front of you, the students in your class, or even anything you might experience that results from their personal behavior. It talks to the limitless part of you: your kundalini energy, your consciousness.

Perhaps more essential for our purposes, Kundalini Yoga is for everyday people. This path is for anyone who wants to learn how to successfully navigate the day-to-day challenges and stresses of life—growing and sustaining families in the shadow of institutionalized roadblocks like the school-to-prison pipeline, juggling that with working at or managing businesses, trying to stay healthy in food deserts, striving to thrive rather than merely survive in a world that often seems to punish us when we dare to act upon aspirations for a fulfilled, successful, and happy life. And so I view it at this time as another way toward healing the underserved communities of color in particular.

The meditations have specific applications, addressing just about every human situation or condition one can name. Developing a positive mind, cultivating creativity, improving relationships, and shifting a foul mood to one of contentment are a few examples. Additionally, there are yoga sets (kriyas) and meditations for healing—to counter high blood pressure, for a healthy thyroid gland, to prevent heart diseases, to eliminate addictions, and to support cognitive function—a few examples of maladies that Kundalini Yoga and meditations can help prevent. However, keep in mind that Kundalini

Yoga is a spiritual practice. It works to make you whole. You are encouraged to approach it with respect and sacredness, beginning with your higher self.

The focus of this book is on meditations that, when practiced regularly, can enable anyone to eliminate negative thought patterns and remain calm under pressure and amid chaos. These techniques will protect you from the stress and strain of the physical world. With the help of this technology, you can find ways to connect with your own higher consciousness, giving you the ability to flow through and around the challenges of the times and to be happy, healthy, and completely holy.

I have divided the meditations into three main sections: for the physical body, for the mental, and for the spiritual. The first section, "Working on the Physical," covers various meditations designed to work on different parts of the body. These exercises help to increase physical strength and flexibility, improve circulation and digestion, and stimulate the glands and organs. The second section, "Working on the Mental," brings meditations that help calm the mind, clear stagnant emotions, reduce stress, and increase mental clarity and focus. The third, "Working on the Spiritual," shares practices that are designed to activate the energy centers in the body, raise the level of consciousness, and connect with your higher Self. By dividing the practices into these three main aspects, I trust this can support you in developing a holistic view of your whole being.

But what is the "evolution" referred to in the book title? Who are these evolving people, and what is the nature of their growth? **We are the evolving ones!** We are moving from an age of finding and acquiring information to one in which everything we want to know is at our fingertips, and we want to apply it. We want to experience it. A lot of what we want to know is about ourselves. We wish to expand and access that limitless part of ourselves. We want to strengthen our sensory selves. This evolution, quite simply, leads to our liberation and our ability to know how the attributes of God are revealed in us.

In Ancient Kemet, also known as Egypt, the words "Man Know Thyself" appear above the entrances of temples in the Nile Valley. These served as academic and scientific learning centers that were not separated from the spiritual. Of course, the term "man" here includes all humans. It is an instruction that encourages all humankind to discover their true nature. "The body is the temple of the God within you," says another ancient adage. Our evolution involves an awareness of our true identities as spiritual beings, resulting in a magnificent shift in consciousness.

Knowing ourselves involves exploring our thoughts, emotions, and experiences and developing a deeper understanding of who we are as a person.

The process of self-discovery is a lifelong journey that requires a great deal of introspection, self-reflection, and self-awareness. It requires an openness to confront our fears and limitations and the courage to make changes in areas where improvement is needed. By becoming more familiar with our own strengths and weaknesses, we can become more confident and resilient, with a greater sense of purpose. By knowing ourselves, we can also develop a deeper sense of inner peace and satisfaction and live a life that is truly authentic and fulfilling.

Yoga and meditation have been recognized for centuries as powerful tools for self-discovery and personal growth. These practices help us connect with our inner selves, become more aware of our thoughts and emotions, and access a deeper level of understanding and insight into our individual nature. They also encourage the integration of the physical, mental, and spiritual aspects of the self. Through the consistent practice of yoga and meditation, we can gain insight into the root causes of negative patterns and work to transform them into more positive and supportive habits. Ultimately, the goal is for us to realize our full potential and live in alignment with our true nature and purpose in life.

Yogi Bhajan once said, "Our purpose in life is to live in higher consciousness and to teach others to live in higher consciousness."[3] He also said, "It is a time for prayer, for deep cleansing, for self-identity, and for self-control. What is honesty? When you can stand against dishonesty. What is reality? When you can stand against non-reality. What is loyalty? When you can stand against betrayal. So, the pair of opposites is there. We have to choose the positive. And we have to make a choice, and that choice can only be made if our psyche is in diagonal energy, the energy that crosses through all levels and is always there to lift us up in any situation in which we can fall."[4]

The meditations in this book are a gift from Yogi Bhajan to all who wish to learn them. It is a gift of inspiration designed to serve the highest good of humankind. In his book co-authored with Gurucharan Singh Khalsa, PhD, *The Mind, Its Projections and Multiple Facets*, Yogi Bhajan said, "We have the fastest and the most wonderful power—our own mind. It can take us to God. It can take us to ourselves. It can take us deep into our self or far out into the universe. When clean and open, the mind can do anything that we want."[5]

3   Yogi Bhajan, *Aquarian Times*, Winter 2005.

4   Yogi Bhajan, *The Library of Teachings*, February 4, 2001.

5   Yogi Bhajan and Gurucharan Singh, *The Mind, Its Projections and Multiple Facets*, Kundalini Research Institute: 1998, p. 65.

A Special Note to Black People of the Diaspora

GETTING MORE PEOPLE OF COLOR ON THE YOGA MAT

Collectively, we have lived under stressful conditions for quite a long time. There was no preparation for enslavement, and no debriefing sessions were held during or after its end. It was a Maafa[6], a horrific, traumatic experience with present-day consequences of institutionalized and repercussive natures. These include the constant threats of violence against black bodies in the present day—echoes of the past. There are often microaggressions in the workplace, and the stress of shifting neighborhoods and uneven playing fields affects many aspects of life.

Studies are showing that melanated people are more likely to die at an early age from all causes and that our youth are developing the diseases of old people at a very young age. This can be your reality when you are a person of color. Racism and its stressors have been proven to have a damaging impact on health, increasing the risk of various disease, and mortality, such as hypertension, breast cancer, depression, cardiovascular disease and the common cold, as highlighted in a dedicated issue of *The American Journal of Public Health*[7]. "Embodied inequality," a term coined by researcher Nancy Krieger, refers to the impact of the fear or anticipation of discrimination on our stress response systems. Even if someone isn't directly experiencing racism, exposure to it can still pose health risks.

It is indeed very challenging to live in a positive present when negativities from the past and stressors like microaggressions and other blatant and subtle forms of systemic racism seem to be a constant intrusion. However, it does not have to define people of color or be a perpetual reality. It does not have to be the center of our attention.

Sound the alarm: Let us focus attention on our health. Let these be the focal points: balanced mental, spiritual, physical, and economic health. We have the option of focusing on what we want rather than what we don't want. We want spiritual health, happiness, and abundance of all kinds. We deserve it. Most importantly, it is our birthright.

---

6   Maafa, African Holocaust, Holocaust of Enslavement, or Black Holocaust are political terms used to describe the history and ongoing effects of mistreatment of African people, especially by non-African groups such as Europeans and Arabs. This mistreatment has been primarily related to slavery. These forms of oppression persist to this day through imperialism, colonialism, and other means.

7   For more detailed information on other researches, see "Why Black Business People Should Meditate", in: *Black Enterprise*. June 6, 2016 http://www.blackenterprise.com/black-business-people-meditate/

Rather than living in the past and fearing the future, we can work to master ourselves now. However, it will require letting go of a lot of stuff. It will require accessing the contents of those dark recesses of the mind, which are constantly fed reminders of a traumatic past and an often challenging present. It requires a steady discipline of focusing on each present moment and allowing attached emotions and commotions that are blocking personal and collective progress to be released. It requires creating new, positive thought patterns. It requires lots of inner work and a reconnection to the world of spirit.

Kundalini Yoga and meditation are vehicles through which personal transcendence can be achieved, leading to collective ascendancy. It is not a religion. Though references to God are often made, you can replace it with whatever name you relate to – the Great I Am, the Infinite One, the Creator, and Source of all things. Kundalini Yoga works to awaken the kundalini energy present at the base of the spine. Tapping into this energy purifies your system and brings about complete awareness of your body. It gets rid of mental and spiritual blocks. It works to prevent many of the physical diseases found to be common in our communities while improving upon existing negative conditions impacting our bodies. As Yogi Bhajan once put it, "Kundalini Yoga is the science to unite the finite with Infinity, and it's the art to experience Infinity in the finite."[8]

Studies show that yoga and meditation are beneficial to health and well-being in general. Kundalini Yoga and meditation address many of the mental and spiritual conditions and diseases that disproportionately affect people of color[9]. Various scientific studies conducted by Harvard's Division of Sleep Medicine's Dr. Sat Bir Singh Khalsa and other prominent researchers have repeatedly demonstrated that yoga and meditation are effective tools for managing stress and its related side effects[10]. It leads to physical health improvements such as better immune function, lower inflammation, regulated blood pressure, improved circulation, reduced cortisol levels, and decreased pain. It also has a positive impact on mental health, including increased happiness, emotional regulation, and self-control, as well as decreased depression,

---

8 Yogi Bhajan, *The Library of Teaching*, October 27, 1988.

9 Several black women have turned to yoga to improve their health. In a search of over 200 published black women's memoirs, the term "yoga" appeared in 42 narratives. For more, see "Yoga in 42 African American women's memoirs reveal hidden tradition of health", in: *International Journal of Yoga*. Retrieved July 31, 2018 from https://www.ncbi.nlm.nih.gov/pmc/articles/PMC4728966/

10 See Sat Bir Singh Khalsa articles on Kundalini Yoga and meditations at https://kundaliniresearchinstitute.org/en/yoga-research/

anxiety, and the risk of addiction. Furthermore, meditation has been shown to have a positive impact on brain structure, with increased gray matter in areas related to self-regulation and thicker cortical areas for better attention.

You are all encouraged to get on the mat, do yoga, and meditate[11]. Give yourself the opportunity to release the obstacles that block you and the ties that bind you. Improve your quality of life, align, connect with your higher self, and connect with the God in you! Use this technology that is available to everyone. Achieve liberation while alive!

Saving Mothers and Babies: Rewriting the Narrative

There's no doubt about it: people of the African diaspora are resilient. In our historical times, in our homelands, in antiquity and beyond— before enslavement—our spirituality, sense of community, and purpose were what made and kept us strong. Today, despite the best efforts of the colonizers to break our spirit, we thrive.

But the constant, systemic racism has torn a hole in our society that we need to fix right away because it hurts our women and children and, by extension, may hurt our future generations if we don't deal with it and turn things around. Dr. Arline Geronimus, a professor in the Department of Health Behavior and Health Education at the University of Michigan School of Public Health, has linked stress to high African American maternal and infant mortality. She calls her theory "weathering." She believes that a kind of toxic stress triggers the premature deterioration of the bodies of African American women as a consequence of repeated exposure to a climate of racism and a variety of repeated slights and insults. The weathering of the black mother's body, she theorized, could lead to poor pregnancy outcomes, including the death of her infant.

Dr. Geronimus' research has shown that the societal and systemic racism faced by black women creates a toxic stress, leading to higher rates of infant and maternal death, which are worsened by a pervasive racial bias in the healthcare system. This bias can result in dismissed concerns and symptoms. Even black women with advanced degrees are more likely to lose their babies, demonstrating that this disparity is not only based on income or education. Today, black infants are still more likely to die than white infants, with black women being three to four times more likely to die from pregnancy-related causes. A 2017

---

11 See "Yoga and Black Men, Why Brothers Should Make the Stretch", in *Ebony Magazine*. December 11, 2019. Accessed on June 20th, 2023 https://www.ebony.com/black-men-yoga/

report from the Department of Health and Human Services found that pre-eclampsia and eclampsia are 60% more common and severe in African-American women[12]. This is a disparity that has persisted throughout history and was also highlighted by W.E.B. Du Bois in his 1899 book, "The Philadelphia Negro." Du Bois discussed the tragedy of black infant death and persistent racial disparities and even shared the death of his own son in "The Souls of Black Folk."

In 1997, researchers from Boston and Howard universities working on the Black Women's Health Study indicated that women who reported the highest experiences of racism had higher rates of preterm birth. This confirms that the level of stress that Black women face on a daily basis is similar to the bone-deep triggering experience of trauma. "When a person is faced with a threat, the brain responds to the stress by releasing a flood of hormones, which allow the body to adapt and respond to the challenge. When stress is sustained, long-term exposure to stress hormones can lead to wear and tear on the cardiovascular, metabolic, and immune systems, making the body vulnerable to illness and even early death," writes Linda Villarosa in an extensive article on the subject for *The New York Times Magazine*.[13]

According to an article by Geronimus and her colleagues for *The American Journal of Public Health*, African-American women have higher allostatic load scores compared to white women and black men, even after adjusting for factors such as income and education. Allostatic load scores are a measurement of stress-related chemicals in the body and their impact on the body's systems. "These effects may be felt particularly by black women because of [the] double jeopardy of gender and racial discrimination."[14]

Let us focus on using every tool at our disposal to turn this situation around. Kundalini Yoga and meditation are two tools that anyone can use, from birth to the last breath.

---

12   For more, see Hunter, Purvis Lashieka, "The Womb Whisperers: Why More Pregnant Women Are Hiring Doulas", in: Essence. Retrieved October 24, 2019 from https://www.essence.com/lifestyle/health-wellness/doulas-why-more-pregnant-women-hiring-womb-whisperer/

13   Villarosa, Linda. "Why America's Black Mothers and Babies Are in a Life-or-Death Crisis", in *The New York Times Magazine*. April 11, 2018. For more, see "Black Mothers Respond to Our Cover Story on Maternal Mortality", in: *The New York Times*. Retrieved June 25, 2019 from https://www.nytimes.com/2018/04/19/magazine/black-mothers-respond-to-our-cover-story-on-maternal-mortality.html

14   Ibidem.

Control Your Breath, Control Your Mind

The slower your rate of breathing, the more control you have over your mind. Why? The mind follows the breath. When you are stressed, your breathing rate increases or becomes irregular, which makes it difficult for the mind to perform optimally. Your body reacts by following the mind and going into fight or flight. In other words, it gets into survival mode: your heart rate speeds up and the nervous system reacts.

To control your breath, remember these principles:

» Your rate of breathing and your state of mind are inseparable.

» The slower your rate of breathing, the more control you have over your mind.

» The mind follows the breath, and the body follows the mind.
Breathing slowly and steadily calms the mind. As you practice the meditations in this book, be aware of your breath. Below are instructions for the breathing techniques (pranayama) that you will use in this book. Most of the meditations require only automatic breathing, the breathing pattern that occurs naturally as you practice a meditation. However, some meditations require specific breathing techniques.

LONG DEEP BREATHING

This is one of the most important breathing techniques in Kundalini Yoga. You are breathing through the nose. Start by filling the abdomen with air, then inhaling into and expanding the chest, and finally lifting the upper ribs and clavicles (collar bones). The exhale is reversed: first the upper boddy deflates, then the middle, and finally the abdomen pulls in and up as the Navel Point pulls gently back toward the spine.

THE BENEFITS:

» Relaxes and calms you due to its influence on the parasympathetic nervous system[15].

» Increases the flow of praana, your life force energy.

---

15   The parasympathetic system conserves energy as it slows the heart rate, increases intestinal and gland activity, and relaxes sphincter muscles in the gastrointestinal tract. It is balanced by the Sympathetic Nervous system which does the opposite.

» Reduces and prevents the build-up of toxins in the lungs by encouraging the clearing of the small air sacs (alveoli).

» Stimulates the brain chemicals (endorphins) that help fight depression.

» Brings the brain to a new level of alertness.

» Pumps the spinal fluid to the brain, giving it greater energy.

» Stimulates the pituitary gland to secrete, which enhances intuition.

» Filling the lungs to capacity revitalizes and re-adjusts the magnetic field.

» Cleanses the blood.

» Regulates the body's pH balance, which affects the ability to handle stressful situations.

» Energizes and increases vitality.

» Aids in releasing blockages in meridian energy flow.

» Activates and clears the nerve channels.

» Aids in speeding up emotional and physical healing.

» Breaks down subconscious negative thought patterns like insecurities and fears.

» Aids in fighting addictions.

» Re-channels previous mental conditioning on pain, resulting in the reduction or elimination of pain.

» Gives the capacity to manage negativity and emotions, supporting clarity, patience, and a cool head.

SEGMENTED BREATHS

With segmented breathing, the inhalation and exhalation are divided into several equal parts, with a slight suspension of the breath separating each part and a distinct beginning and end point for each segment. This stimulates the central brain and the glandular system in different ways. Instead of inhaling in one smooth motion, we break the breath up into segmented "sniffs." Try not to collapse, squeeze the nostrils in on the sniff, or pull the breath too deeply into the lungs. The goal is for the breath to strike a relaxed yet focused area in the nasal passage to stimulate a particular set of nerves. Keep the nostrils relaxed and direct the attention to the feel of the breath further along the air passages and to the motion of the diaphragm.

 » 4 parts in, 1 part out: healing, energizing, uplifting;

 » 4 parts in, 4 parts out: clarity, alertness, triggering glands;

 » 8 parts in, 8 parts out: calming, centering;

 » 8 parts in, 4 parts out: focusing, energizing;

 » 4 parts in, 8 parts out: calming, unblocking, letting go.

The ratios used in Kundalini Yoga are clearly defined. They are specific and create stable, predictable, and final states of mind and energy. It is best not to experiment since not all ratios are balanced or sustainable. When it comes to segmented breath, more is not better. Therefore, do not create your own ratios.

THE 15-SECOND BREATH

"The longer and deeper your breath is, the more your psyche attracts everything to you—it's a way to prosperity." – Yogi Bhajan[16]

Start by being relaxed. You don't want to rush the 5-second intervals of the 15-second breath. Inhale slowly and steadily, filling your lower abdomen and your stomach area, going up to your chest area, and then all the way up to the clavicles (collar bones). After 5 seconds, lock your breath once you've filled your upper chest up to your clavicle. Suspend the breath for 5 seconds. Then

---

16   Bhajan, Yogi. *Success and the Spirit: An Aquarian Path to Abundance*, Kundalini Research Institute, 2011, p. 199.

exhale slowly, gently, and steadily, taking 5 seconds to do so. At the end of the last 5 seconds, gently reverse to an inhale and begin again. Note that this is not a segmented breath. You are inhaling slowly and steadily, rather than sniffing.

SUSPENDING THE BREATH

Oftentimes, students are asked to suspend the breath during a kriya or meditation. Suspending the breath means relaxing the muscles of the diaphragm, ribs, and abdomen that are responsible for the breath's constant motion. It will support deep internal self-transformation. The beauty of suspending the breath is that when we become aware of the dynamics of how the physical apparatus of respiration works, the mystery of breath is revealed.

To suspend the breath on the inhale, begin by inhaling deeply. Bring the attention to the clavicles and upper ribs. Lift the upper ribs slightly and fix them in place. Relax the shoulders, throat, and face. Pull the chin in. Become still and calm. If you feel the urge to exhale, inhale a tiny bit instead.

To suspend the breath on the exhale, start with a complete exhale. Pull the Navel Point back towards the spine, lift the lower chest and diaphragm, and let the upper ribs relax and compress. Do not bend the spine and ribs when you try to exhale completely—that would interrupt the action of the diaphragm. Pull the chin in and become still and calm. If the muscles start to reflexively inhale, consciously exhale a little more. This can extend the length of suspension significantly without any strain or struggle.

The goal of suspending the breath is the gradual reconditioning of the nervous system. Breath suspension allows for integration of the body's systems. Suspending the breath in can temporarily raise some blood pressure. Suspending out lowers the blood pressure and relaxes the circulation. Suspending in impacts the sympathetic nervous system; suspending out impacts the parasympathetic nervous system.

Suspending the breath allows for centering and training in the use of good judgment under pressure. On the suspended breath, you can experience *shuniya*, which is a deep stillness, into which you can plant a seed (a *bij*) to create a new rhythm or pattern of being. In *shuniya*, the Kundalini flows.

POINTS TO REMEMBER WHEN SUSPENDING THE BREATH:

> » The brain will trigger inhalation when the carbon dioxide (CO_2) level in the blood rises too high. It does not react to a loss or gain of

oxygen. The cue is taken from the CO_2 level. If you prepare to suspend the breath by taking several complete exhales and blowing out extra CO_2, you will suspend the breath longer and with more comfort.

» If you begin to experience dizziness or disorientation, stop. Dizziness is not enlightenment! If you have high blood pressure, do not suspend your breath for more than 10 seconds. You must build this practice with determination, regularity and patience. Pushing past your capacity will not benefit you.

» Throughout your practice, create a calm internal spot in your awareness to observe the changes in the body and mind.

» In all practices where the breath is suspended in or out, remember that the goal is a switch in metabolic activity, nervous system balance, or emotional control.

Common Kundalini Yoga Mudras and Their Energetic Properties

Mudra is a specific positioning of the hands in order to give clear messages to the mind-body energy system. Each area of the hand corresponds to a certain area of the body and to different emotions and behaviors. Curling, crossing, stretching, and touching the fingers and palms allow us to communicate with the body and mind with specific intention. Here are some of the most common hand positions that you'll see throughout this book. In all mudras, the thumb represents the ego.

GYAN MUDRA
(SEAL OF KNOWLEDGE)
Touch the tips of the Jupiter (index) fingers and the tips of the thumbs. The other three fingers are straight. This mudra stimulates knowledge, wisdom, receptivity, and calmness. It's related to the planet Jupiter and to expansion.

SHUNI MUDRA
(SEAL OF PATIENCE)

Touch the tips of the Saturn (middle) fingers and the tips of the thumbs. The other three fingers are straight. It promotes patience, discernment, and commitment. It's related to Saturn and to the qualities of a taskmaster, taking responsibility and having the courage to hold on to duty.

SURYA OR RAVI MUDRA
(SEAL OF LIFE)

Touch the tips of the Sun (ring) fingers and the tips of the thumbs. The other three fingers are straight. It revitalizes energy, strengthens the nerves, and promotes good health. It's related to the Sun and Uranus and their qualities of energy, health, and sexuality; nerve strength, intuition, and change.

BUDDHI MUDRA
(SEAL OF MENTAL CLARITY)

Touch the tips of the Mercury (little) and the tips of the thumbs. The other three fingers are straight. It creates the capacity to clearly and intuitively communicate and stimulates psychic development. It's related to Mercury and its qualities of quickness and mental powers of communication.

PRAYER POSE (PRANAM MUDRA)

The palms of both hands and fingers are completely touching. The outer edge of the mound of the thumb is pressed into the sternum. It neutralizes the positive side of the body (right, sun, masculine) with the negative side (left, moon, feminine). Pranam Mudra, or prayer pose, has a science to it. There is a polarity in the body between the right side, the *pingala*, and the left side, the *ida*. When you put the right and left hands together, you neutralize the positive and negative polarities of the electromagnetic field. This action creates a neutral space in the electromagnetic field. The position of the thumb knuckles in the notch of the breastbone is a reflex point for the vagus nerve, one of the major nerves that runs up the front of the body to the pineal gland. This pressure immediately causes the pineal and pituitary glands to secrete, creating a resonance in the brain that moves it out of its normal rhythm and into a meditative state. This allows one's prayer to come from the heart.

VENUS LOCK

This mudra channels the sexual energy, promotes glandular balance, and increases the ability to concentrate easily. For working feminine, reflective energy, interlace the fingers with the right little finger on the bottom. Place the right thumb in the webbing between the thumb and index finger of the left hand. The left thumb presses the fleshy mound at the base of the right thumb. For working with masculine, projective energy, the thumb positions are reversed, and the left little finger goes on the bottom. The mounds at the base of the thumbs represent Venus and the qualities of sensuality and sexuality.

Before You Begin

If you're new to Kundalini Yoga, note that it's always a good practice to tune in before you begin your yoga each day. Here, we share key points to be aware of when doing the practices below.

TUNING IN

Every Kundalini Yoga session begins with chanting the Adi Mantra[17], "Ong Namo Guru Dev Namo." By chanting it with the right pronunciation and projection, the student becomes open to their higher self, the source of all guidance, and accesses the protective link between himself or herself and the consciousness of the divine teacher.

Sit in a comfortable cross-legged position with the spine straight. Place the palms of the hands together as if in prayer, with the fingers pointing straight up, and then press the joints of the thumbs into the center of the chest at the sternum. Inhale deeply. Focus your concentration on the Third Eye Point. As you exhale, chant the entire mantra in one breath. If you can't chant on a single breath, then take a quick sip of air through the mouth after "Ong Namo" and then chant the rest of the mantra, extending the sound as long as possible. As you chant "Ong", let the sound

---

17   "Adi" means primal or first. Thus, Adi Mantra is the first or primal mantra.

vibrate the inner chambers of the sinuses and the upper palate to create a mild pressure at the Third Eye Point. The mouth is slightly open, and the lips held firm, increasing the resonance while the sound comes out through the nose. The sound "Dev" is chanted a minor third higher than the other sounds of the mantra. Chant this mantra at least three times before beginning your Kundalini Yoga practice.

The "O" sound in Ong is long, as in "go," and of short duration. The "ng" sound is long and produces a definite vibration on the roof of the mouth and the cranium. The "O," as in "go," is held longer. The first syllable of Guru is pronounced as in the word "good." The second syllable rhymes with "true." The first syllable is short, and the second one is long. The word Dev rhymes with "gave."

"Ong" is the infinite creative energy experienced in manifestation and activity. It is a variant of the cosmic syllable "Om," which refers to God in its absolute or unmanifest state. "Namo" has the same root as the Sanskrit word "Namaste," which means reverent greetings. It implies bowing with reverence. Together, "Ong Namo" means "I call on the infinite creative consciousness," and it opens you to the universal consciousness that guides all action. "Guru" is the embodiment of the wisdom that one is seeking. "Dev" means higher, subtle, or divine. It refers to the spiritual realms. "Namo," at the end of the mantra, reaffirms the humble reverence of the student. Taken together, "Guru Dev Namo" means, "I call on the divine wisdom," whereby you bow before your higher self to guide you in using the knowledge and energy given by the cosmic self.

MENTAL FOCUS
Meditation requires concentration. To receive the benefits of each meditation you will need to mentally focus. To assist you, the instructions for each meditation will tell you where to focus your concentration with your eyes. Unless you are directed to do otherwise, close your eyes and focus at the Third Eye Point. It is located between the eyebrows, where the root of the nose meets the skull bone.

Mentally locate this point by gently turning your eyes upward and inward. Remain aware of your breath, your posture, your hand position(s), your movements, and any mantra that may accompany the meditation. Be aware of it all as you center your awareness at the place of focus. This may sound like a lot at first. However, as with anything, the more you do it, the more it becomes second nature. Meditation is a process. Be patient with yourself.

BREATH WITH MANTRA
Mantra are repeated sounds that direct and focus the mind. They are words of

power. Mantra enables you to easily keep up during challenging exercises or meditations. The simplest movements have depth when mantra is applied. The power of the mantra is maximized when it is linked with your breath cycle. For example, Sat Naam – rhymes with "But Mom"– is a common mantra that means "Truth is my identity." Mentally repeat "Sat" on the inhale and "Naam" on the exhale. This will allow you to screen your thoughts so that each thought is a positive one.

PACING YOURSELF

Kundalini Yoga exercises may involve rhythmic movement between two or more postures. Begin slowly, keeping a steady rhythm. Then increase gradually as the body allows, being careful not to strain. Be sure that the spine has become warm and flexible before attempting rapid movements. It is important to be aware of your body and responsible for its well-being.

CONCLUDING AN EXERCISE

Unless it says otherwise, an exercise ends by inhaling and suspending the breath for a short time, then exhaling and relaxing the posture. While the breath is being held, apply the Root Lock[18], contracting the muscles around the anal sphincter, the sex organs, and the Navel Point, while drawing the navel back towards the spine. This consolidates the effects of any exercise and circulates the energy to your higher centers. Suspend the breath just beyond a level of comfort. If you experience any discomfort, immediately release the lock and exhale.

ENDING A YOGA PRACTICE

To close up a yoga practice, sit up straight and put the palms together, with the thumbs pointing up and resting against the sternum. Inhale deeply and chant the mantra **SAT NAAM** three times ("Sat" lasts 7 seconds, "Naam" 1 second). The mantra means "Truth is my name" or "my true identity." This mantra connects you with your soul and your destination.

In Kundalini yoga classes or when practicing alone, we sing a short song before chanting three long Sat Naam. The song is an inspiring prayer for the rest of your day. It says: "May the Long Time Sun Shine Upon You, All Love Surround You, And the Pure Light Within You Guide Your Way On."[19]

---

18   The Root Lock is like a hydraulic lock at the base of the spine. It coordinates, stimulates, and balances the energies involved with the rectum, sex organs, and Navel Point (i.e., the lower three chakras).

19   You can find a beautiful version of this chant on the internet or go to the Gurbani Media Center from Sikhnet at sikhnet.com/gurbani/

WORKING ON THE PHYSICAL

"I MADE A COMMITMENT TO COMPLETELY
CUT OUT DRINKING AND ANYTHING THAT
MIGHT HAMPER ME FROM GETTING MY MIND
AND BODY TOGETHER. AND THE FLOODGATES
OF GOODNESS HAVE OPENED UPON ME–
SPIRITUALLY AND FINANCIALLY"
DENZEL WASHINGTON, ACTOR

When we create and sustain a healthy body, we are ready to receive the gifts that life offers. These gifts include happiness, inner peace, centeredness, self-knowledge, and connection to the One Most High. It is difficult to give attention to happier pursuits when our focus must be on ill health.

It is interesting to note that in traditional African societies, coronary artery disease is almost nonexistent. However, rates among African Americans are similar to those of white Americans. This suggests that diet and lifestyle play an important role[20]. Diabetes, stroke, heart disease, and many forms of cancer are preventable diseases. Kundalini Yoga offers exercise sets that can give one flexibility, increased lung capacity, a strengthened nervous and immune system, purification of the blood, and so much more.

Enjoy your journey of healing and nurturing your physical body with the following practices!

20   "Chapter 44 Prevention of Chronic Disease by Means of Diet and Lifestyle Changes," National Library of Medicine, accessed February 17, 2023, htttps://www.ncbi.nlm.nih.gov/books/NBK11795/

Meditation for the Physical Body[21]

April 7, 1972

Sit in Easy Pose with a straight spine and a light Neck Lock.

Mudra: Relax the right hand in Gyan Mudra on the right knee, keeping the elbow straight. Raise the left hand 6 inches (15 cm) in front of the Heart Center with the palm facing the chest and the fingers pointing to the right. Chant **I AM** and emphasize "**I**" as you draw the hand closer to 4 inches (10 cm) in front of the Heart Center. Chant **I AM** and emphasize "**AM**" as you move the hand straight out from the body to 12 inches (30 cm) at the Heart Center level. Take a breath as you return the hand to the original position of 6 inches (15 cm) in front of the Heart Center.

Eye Focus: 1/10th open, look straight ahead through the eyelids.

Breath: Inhale as you draw the hand into the original position 6 inches (15 cm) in front of the Heart Center, exhale naturally as you chant. Create a steady rhythm with the mantra and the breath.

Mantra: I AM, I AM.

Time: 11-31 minutes.

To End: Inhale deeply, suspend the breath, exhale and relax.

21   Originally published as "Meditation into Being: I Am I Am"

Comments: This mantra connects the finite and infinite identities and dissolves duality. The first "I Am" that emphasizes the "I" is the personal and finite sense of self. The second "I Am" that emphasizes slightly the "Am" is the impersonal and transcendent sense of the Self. Being who you are is the essence of truth and will lead you to the nature of reality. The hand and the breath move in rhythm and strengthen your ability to maintain a sense of self as your awareness expands. A yogi cultivates the relationship between the finite sense of the self and the infinite sense of the Self. The mind often forgets this relationship when it becomes attached to a particular emotion or object that it wants to keep. One of the important habits the yogi instills in the mind is the ability to break that trance of attachment by shifting to the perspective of Infinity. This is also the perspective of Being. You exist before the objects you collect and even before the body that you use. It is very powerful and effective to remind the mind of your true identity with your Infinite Being. What the yogi seeks is to participate in life with authenticity and wholeness.

Author's Note: This meditation brings home the fact that we are more than just our physical selves. We have the inner experience of God available to us.

Meditation for Healing Addictions and Eliminating Negative Habits

Originally published in the Aquarian Teacher Yoga Manual

Sit in Easy Pose with a straight spine and a light Neck Lock.

Mudra: Make fists of both hands with the thumbs extended. Raise the arms with the elbows stretched to the sides. Place the thumbs on the temples in the niche where they fit. This is the lower anterior portion of the frontal bone above the temporal-sphenoidal suture. Keep the lips closed and lock the back molars together. Keeping the molars pressed together throughout, alternately squeeze and release the pressure. A muscle will move under the thumbs.

Eye Focus: Third Eye Point.

Breath: Not specified.

Mantra: Mentally chant the Panj Shabd **SAA TAA NAA MAA**[22] at the Third Eye Point. Synchronize the squeezing action of the molars with the mantra, 1 squeeze per syllable.

Time: 5-7 minutes. With practice, the time can be increased to **20 minutes** and ultimately to **31 minutes**.

Comments: The pressure exerted by the thumbs triggers a rhythmic reflexive current into the central

22   These sounds express the five primal sounds of the Universe (S, M, T, N and A). It describes the continuous cycle of life and creation and is the atomic form of the mantra "Sat Naam". It increases intuition and balances the hemispheres of the brain.

brain. This current stimulates the area directly underneath the stem of the pineal gland. Yogically, it is an imbalance in this area that makes mental and physical addictions seem unbreakable. Imbalance in this pineal area upsets the radiance of the pineal gland itself. It is this pulsating radiance that regulates the pituitary gland. Since the pituitary regulates the rest of the glandular system, the entire body and mind go out of balance. In modern culture, this imbalance is pandemic. If we are not only addicted to smoking, eating, drinking, or drugs, then we are also subconsciously addicted to acceptance, advancement, rejection, emotional love, etc. All of these lead us to insecure and neurotic behavior patterns. This meditation is excellent for everyone but particularly effective for rehabilitation efforts in drug dependence, mental illness, and phobic conditions.

Author's Note: In these times, there are many addictions to be had. Unfortunately, they are rampant in underserved communities. Smoking, eating, drinking, and doing drugs are some familiar ones. There are also emotional addictions that may be of a subconscious nature, such as negative attention, negative self-talk, rejection, emotional love, etc. Then there are the addictions to electronics and social media. What do they have in common? All of them lead to insecure and neurotic behavior patterns.

Two Exercises for Thyroid Gland[23]

July 21, 1977

PART ONE
Stand straight with the knees and heels together and the feet angled out to the sides.

Mudra: Stretch the arms up straight hugging the ears, with palms facing forward (the thumbs can be locked together). Keeping the legs straight, bend back from the base of the spine 20 degrees. The head, spine and arms form an unbroken curve, with the arms remaining in a line with the ears.

Eye Focus: Not specified.

Breath: Long Deep Breathing.

Time: 2 minutes.

Comments: This exercise is called "Miracle Bend." It bends the negativity in the human being. It adjusts the Navel Point and helps bring an emotional and angry person to calmness. There is an automatic tendency to shake in this posture.

---

23   These two stand-alone exercises were taken from the "Kriya Emotional and Mental Balance and Prevention of Early Menopause".

PART TWO
Remain standing with knees and heels together and arms hugging the ears.

Mudra: Very slowly bend forward as far as possible without bending the knees. Keep the arms straight and close to the ears.

Eye Focus: Not specified.

Breath: Inhale deeply, suspend the breath as long as possible while pumping the navel, then exhale, suspend the breath as long as possible, and pump the navel.

Time: 2 minutes.

Author's Note: This meditation promotes healthy thyroid and parathyroid glands. Along with the parathyroid gland, the thyroid gland is the guardian of health and beauty. Improper balance of these two glands can make you age before your time. The thyroid affects the skin, the complexion, and the outward appearance. Other benefits are the promotion of emotional and mental balance, support to prevent early menopause, adjustment of the Navel Point (the area located from above the navel to the breastbone) and soothing feelings of anger into calmness.

Meditation to Strengthen the Pancreas

Originally published in Meditation as Medicine

PART ONE
Sit on your heels in Rock Pose.

Mudra: Cross the hands over your navel, and bring the forehead to the ground, and raise the buttocks up to 60 degrees. The spine is straight.

Eye Focus: Closed, focused on sending energy to the pancreas.

Breath: Long Deep Breathing.

Time: 3 minutes.

To End: Inhale deeply, suspend the breath for **10 seconds**, and exhale.

PART TWO
Remain in Rock Pose.

Mudra: Cross the hands on the Solar Plexus and lean back 60 degrees from the ground. Keep the spine straight and a light Neck Lock.

Eye Focus: Closed, focused on sending energy to the pancreas.

Breath: Long Deep Breathing.

Time: 3 minutes.

To End: Inhale deeply, suspend the breath for **10 seconds**, exhale and relax.

Comments: This meditation helps control blood sugar.

Meditation for the Lower Triangle

Originally published in Sadhana Guidelines

Sit in Easy Pose with a straight spine and a light Neck Lock.

Mudra: Touch the thumbs to the fleshy mound at the base of the Mercury (little) fingers and keep the other fingers straight. Raise the right arm straight up, hugging the ear with the hand facing forward. Raise the left arm straight forward and up to a 60-degree angle from horizontal, with the wrist straight and the palm facing downward. Stretch the arms from the shoulders and keep the elbows straight.

Eye Focus: 1/10th open and look down toward the upper lip.

Breath: The breath will automatically become longer and deeper.

Time: 11 minutes.

Comments: This meditation alleviates problems in the lower spine, heart, kidneys, and adrenal glands. It restores the energy drained by long-term stress.

Meditation to Balance and Recharge the Nervous and Immune Systems

March 23, 1987

PART ONE
Sit in Easy Pose with a straight spine and a light Neck Lock.

Mudra: Lock the Sun (ring) and Mercury (little) fingers of the right hand down with the thumb, the Jupiter (index) and Saturn (middle) fingers are together and extended. Stretch the right arm parallel to the ground and at a 60-degree angle from the centerline of the body, with the hand facing to the left. Extend the left arm out to the side parallel to the ground with the hand facing down, fingers together, and thumb relaxed. Keep the right hand still and stiff, like an iron rod. Move the left arm up and down approximately 9 inches (23 cm) total. Move from the shoulder as fast as possible.

Eye Focus: Third Eye Point.

Breath: Breathe rapidly with the movement of the left arm, it will naturally become a Breath of Fire.

Time: 9 ½ minutes.

To End: Mentally focus on the affirmation "I am the Lord of the Universe" and focus at the Third Eye Point. Inhale deeply, suspend the breath for **30 seconds**. Inhale deeply, suspend the breath for **20 seconds**, tense every part of the body, and exhale. Inhale and exhale quickly **2 times**. Relax.

PART TWO
Remain in Easy Pose with a straight spine and a light Neck Lock.

Mudra: Clasp the hands firmly together in front of the Heart Center, with the left hand closer to the body. Raise the elbows up with forearms parallel to the ground.

Breath: Inhale deeply, suspend the breath for **15 seconds**, press the hands together with so much force that the rib cage shakes, and exhale. Repeat **2 more times**.

Comments: This exercise brings the navel area into balance and recharges all the pranic centers and the immune system of the body. It will put you into a deep meditative state, even if done only for a few minutes. This meditation is for the spine and balances the three nervous systems of the body – parasympathetic, sympathetic, and voluntary. It will slowly and steadily build very strong, steel-like stamina in you. You'll think better, act better, and be more intuitive.

Author's Note: Our nervous and immune systems can take a beating due to the many stressors that abound on this physical plane on a daily basis. "Keep up and you'll be kept up," Yogi Bhajan encourages. We must stay on top of our health and well-being. Practicing with a group encourages this.

Meditation to Strengthen the Nervous System[24]

September 29, 1975

Sit in Easy Pose with a straight spine and a light Neck Lock.

Mudra: With the elbows at the sides of the body, relax the shoulders and raise the forearms up in front of the chest, approximately 7-8 inches (18-20 cm) in front of the nipples, palms facing each other, and the fingers pointing forward. To work with masculine projective energy, place the right hand in Shuni Mudra by touching the tips of the Saturn (middle) finger and thumb, and place the left hand in Buddhi Mudra by touching the tips of the Mercury (little) finger and thumb. Fingernails don't touch. To work with feminine reflective energy, hold the mudra with opposite hands (right hand in Buddhi Mudra and left hand in Shuni Mudra).

Eye Focus: 1/10 open.

Breath: Normal.

Time: 11 minutes.

To End: Inhale, make tight fists with both hands for a few moments, exhale and relax.

Comments: This meditation works to balance the brain by reinforcing your continual connection with your higher Self. This meditation strengthens the nervous system. It

24   This meditation was formerly known as "Meditation to Feel Calm and Cozy".

will create a calm and pleasant feeling
even under the pressures of our minds
and the changes of the Age. It will
create sensitivity and a prosperous
mental horizon within. It develops
a steadiness to act intelligently.

Pranic Meditation for the Heart Center

April 3, 1996

PART ONE
Sit in Easy Pose with a straight spine and a light Neck Lock.

Mudra: Touch the Jupiter (index) finger and thumb of the right hand to the Jupiter finger and thumb of the left hand, creating a triangle-shaped space with the two Jupiter fingers and thumbs. (The better the triangle you can make, the better will be the effect of the meditation.) Curl the other fingers into the palms as in fists. Raise the forearms and place the mudra in front of the Heart Center.

Eye Focus: Closed.

Breath: Long Deep Breathing.

Mental Focus: Concentrate deeply on the breath; do not breathe automatically. On the inhale, imagine the breath bringing in a lot of energy, enriching you. On the exhale, imagine the breath carrying away all of your weaknesses. Breathe with the awareness of the real, living praana in each breath.

Time: 14 ½ minutes.
Immediately begin Part Two.

Comments: During this meditation, your body may feel itchy and interfere with your concentration. Stay steady, keep your focus on the breath, and go through it. Gong was played in the original class for the last 4 ½ minutes. This pranic meditation with

the triangle mudra of the Jupiter fingers works very intensely on the Heart Center. It can keep your brain in good shape, provided that your breath is long, deep and conscious.

PART TWO
Remain in Easy Pose with a straight spine and a light Neck Lock.

Mudra: Interlace the hands on the back of the neck with the elbows stretched out to the sides.

Eye Focus: Not specified.

Breath: Deeply and rapidly inhale and exhale through an "O" mouth.

Time: 1-2 minutes.

To End: Inhale deeply and immediately exhale with a whistle, whistling all the breath out. Repeat **1 more time**. Inhale deeply, suspend the breath for **20 seconds**, and squeeze every muscle, spreading energy to every molecule. Exhale. Relax for **1 minute**.

Comments: The faster and deeper the breath, the more healing you will create.

PART THREE
Remain in Easy Pose with a straight spine and a light Neck Lock.

Mudra: a) Make claws of your hands, contracting and releasing your hands and fingers like a cat scratching.

continue on next page ☞

Continue for **30 seconds**. b) Take some time to talk and socialize for **1-2 minutes** so you can be sure you are ready to resume normal activity. If you are practicing alone, talk to yourself.

Total Time: 1-2 ½ minutes.

Comments: The morning after you practice this meditation, have a glass of fresh lemon juice and water ready by your bedside. When you arise for the day, sip this drink very slowly. This will seal the meditation. Drink through a straw or rinse out your mouth afterward to protect the enamel of your teeth from the acid in the lemon juice.

Meditation to Stimulate Your Chakras

December 20, 1999

Sit in Easy Pose with a straight spine and a light Neck Lock.

Mudra: Place the fingers of the left hand on the forehead with the Mercury (little) finger on the Third Eye Point and the remaining fingers next to each other on the midline. The thumb is relaxed. Extend the right arm from the shoulder straight forward with the palm facing left.

Eye Focus: Closed.

Breath: Slow Long Deep Breathing.

Time: 18 minutes.

To End: Inhale, suspend the breath for **5-10 seconds**, exhale. Repeat **1 more time**. Inhale, interlock the fingers, stretch the arms over the head, elongate the spine, suspend the breath for **10-15 seconds**, exhale. Relax.

Comments: This kriya helps us to handle the pressures of the times. The breath will become longer and more powerful, and you can use the increased praana to give you endurance to go through the pain, to rise above any situation, and to carry you through.

Meditation to Fight Brain Fatigue

March 27, 1995

PART ONE
Sit in Easy Pose with a straight spine and a light Neck Lock.

Mudra: Rest the elbows at the sides of the body. Extend the forearms straight forward, parallel to the ground, with right hand facing down and left hand facing up. On each stroke of the breath, alternately move the hands up and down. One hand moves up as the other hand moves down. The movement of the hands is approximately 6-8 inches (15-20 cm). After **3 minutes**, switch hand positions, left hand facing down and right facing up, and continue for **3 more minutes**; switch hands again, right hand facing down and left hand facing up for **3 more minutes**.

Eye Focus: Not specified.

Breath: Inhale and exhale in 8 strokes through the nose. Breathe powerfully.

Time: 9 minutes total.
Immediately begin Part Two.

PART TWO
Remain in Easy Pose.

Mudra: Hold the mudra from Part One, forearms parallel to the ground, with right hand facing down and left hand facing up. Keep the body perfectly still. Become thoughtless.

Eye Focus: Closed and focused on the Moon Center at the chin.

Breath: Slow Long Deep Breathing.

Time: 5 ½ minutes.

To End: Inhale deeply, suspend the breath for **15 seconds**, make fists and press them strongly against the chest, exhale. Inhale deeply, suspend the breath for **15 seconds**, and press the fists against the Navel Point. Exhale. Inhale deeply, suspend the breath for **15 seconds**, bring the fists to the sides of the shoulders, hands facing forward, and press the upper arms strongly against the rib cage, exhale and relax.

Comments: The movement in this meditation balances the diaphragm and renews the blood supply to the brain, helping to alleviate brain fatigue. It also benefits the lymphatic system.

Meditation for Equilibrium

May 1, 2000

PART ONE
Sit in Easy Pose with a straight spine and a light Neck Lock.

Mudra: Lock the hands into a Bear Grip in front of the Heart Center. The left palm faces out from the chest with the thumb down, and the right palm faces the chest with the thumb up; curl the fingers of the hands into each other. Keep the forearms parallel to the ground. Pull on the Bear Grip without releasing the lock on **HUMEE**, and release on **HUM**. Pull again on **BRAHM** and release on **HUM**. Continue alternating the tension and release in rhythm with the mantra.

Eye Focus: Tip of the Nose.

Breath: Not specified.

Mantra: Chant **HUMEE HUM BRAHM HUM**[25] (The recording by Nirinjan Kaur was played in the original class.)

Time: 11 minutes.

To End: Inhale deeply, exhale and immediately begin Part Two.

---

25   This mantra means "We are we, we are God". It literally means that we are the spirit of God, a total spirit, which represents the Divine Master, and it fixes the identity in its true reality. It can help eliminate the ego consciousness of separation and loss and build faith and trust in the Infinite.

PART TWO
Remain in Easy Pose.

Mudra: Maintain the mudra as in Part One and continue to steadily pull on the Bear Grip.

Eye Focus: Tip of the Nose.

Breath: Long Deep Breathing.

Time: 3 minutes.

To End: Inhale deeply, suspend the breath for **5 seconds**, strongly pull on the lock, and exhale. Repeat **2 more times**.

Comments: Steadily holding the Bear Grip in this part allows the energy created in Part One to circulate through the whole body. Bear Grip creates a balance between the earth's magnetic field and that of the heavens.

Meditation for Self-Healing

May 23, 2000

Sit in Easy Pose with a straight spine and a light Neck Lock.

Mudra: Firmly grasp the back of the neck with the left hand under any loose hair, the left elbow stretched to the side, and upper arm parallel to the ground. Raise the right arm with the elbow stretched to the side, the forearm parallel to the ground, and hand in front of the Heart Center, palm down and fingers together pointing to the left.

Eye Focus: Not specified.

Breath: Not specified.

Mantra: Chant the Siri Gaitri

Mantra: **RAA MAA DAA SAA, SAA SAY SO HUNG**[26]. (Slow version by Joseph Michael Levry was played in the original class.)

Time: 11 minutes.

To End: Inhale deeply, suspend the breath for **25 seconds**, pull the neck forward, resist the pressure and keep the spine straight. Make the body like steel and circulate the energy throughout the body to every organ, every cell. Exhale. Repeat **2 more times** with the breath suspended for **10 seconds**.

---

26   This ashtang mantra is a healing mantra in Kundalini Yoga and is an attunement of the self to the universe. These eight sounds stimulate the kundalini flow in the central channel of the spine for healing.

WORKING ON THE MENTAL

"YOU NEED SO MUCH MORE THAN MENTAL
HEALTH OR 'WELL-BEING' IN THIS ERA
OF DISCRIMINATION, INVISIBILITY, AND
PSYCHOLOGICAL WARFARE. YOU NEED AN
IMPERMEABLE WEB OF PROTECTION FOR
YOUR MIND."
DR. RHEEDA WALKER,
AUTHOR AND PSYCHOLOGIST

Balanced mental health grants us peace of mind. We are able to focus, be stable, grounded, creative, and clear. These days, staying mentally healthy is akin to a form of activism. There are so many systemic, deep-seated inequities, from education to health care to economics and housing to mass incarceration and more. These roadblocks to the happiness that is our birthright have historically weighed heavily. The coverage by mainstream and social media has been a blessing in that it has sparked movements for positive change. However, laid-bare statistics and the readily visible frequency of the atrocities are recipes for depression and other mental health issues in our communities.

A steady practice of Kundalini Yoga and meditation helps you build a web of protection for your mind. It helps you to coordinate the activities of the left and right sides of the brain[27] as well as strengthen the spiritual frontal brain consciousness.

27   Left brain vs. right brain: Fact and fiction, Hammond, Nancy, M.D. Accessed March 4, 2023 at https://www.medicalnewstoday.com/articles/321037#summary

Meditation for Developing an Attitude of Gratitude

December 14, 1977

Sit in Easy Pose with a straight spine and a light Neck Lock.

Mudra: Press the upper arms and elbows firmly on the rib cage. Raise the forearms, bringing the hands together in front of the Heart Center, palms facing up. The outer sides of the Mercury (little) fingers touch, and the hands are slightly cupped.

Eye Focus: 1/10th open and may close during the meditation.

Breath: Allow the breath to self-regulate as you practice.

Mental Focus: Meditate on the boundless flow of the Universal Soul. Imagine something – grace, the light of God, the divine nectar or whatever you believe in – falling into your cupped hands. Sense a deep inflow of spirit. Let it become a reality.

Time: There are no restrictions on the length of time.

Comments: This is a very restful posture. The subtle pressure of the elbows on certain meridian points gives immediate relaxation. This meditation was formerly published as Meditation for Gurprasad. "Gurprasad" means the "gift of the Guru", the universal teacher. As you practice this meditation, allow yourself to receive all of the blessings of the universe – health, wealth, happiness. Fill your heart and soul with all the bounties of nature.

Meditation to Clear the Emotions of the Past

October 10, 1973

Sit in Easy Pose with a straight spine and a light Neck Lock.

Mudra: With the arms relaxed at the sides of the body, bend the elbows and bring the hands in front of the chest, with the tips of the thumbs touching each other and each of the fingers touching the corresponding fingers on the opposite hand. Leave space between the palms. The fingertips are pointing upward.

Eye Focus: Tip of the Nose.

Breath: Breathe 4 times per minute: inhale **5 seconds**, suspend **5 seconds**, exhale **5 seconds**.

Time: 11 minutes (or until you feel relief from the stress).

Comments: This meditation is especially useful for dealing with stressful relationships and past family issues. It addresses phobias, fears, and neuroses. It can remove unsettling thoughts from the past that surface in the present. It can take difficult situations in the present and release them into the hands of Infinity.

Dispel Inner Anger
and Gain Neutral Self

February 15, 2000

PART ONE
Sit in Easy Pose with a straight
spine and a light Neck Lock.

Mudra: Make the hands into tight
fists, with the palms facing the body
and forearms parallel to the ground.
The elbows are slightly away from the
body. Forcefully punch inward, one
fist moving above the other to avoid
hitting each other. Powerfully chant
the mantra **HAR** on each punch.

Eye Focus: Not specified.

Breath: Not specified.

Mantra: HAR.

Time: 7 minutes.

To End: Inhale deeply, suspend the breath for **10-15 seconds,** tighten the fists in front of the body, exhale. Repeat **2 more times.**

Comments: Remember to pull the navel in as you chant and strike the tongue on the roof of the mouth on the rolled "r".

PART TWO
Sit in Easy Pose with a straight spine and a light Neck Lock.

Mudra: Place the hands on the Heart Center.

Eye Focus: Closed.

Breath: Not specified.

Mental Focus: Become calm and meditate on nonexistence.

Time: 4 minutes.

Comments: Only by being neutral can your existence feel the flow of your psyche. We are born to be bright, beautiful, bountiful and blissful.

Author's Note: The goal in yoga practice is not to suppress or deny our anger but to respect it as a primal and potent energy source that can be harnessed and put to work in service of the spirit.

Meditation to Prevent Freaking Out

July 6, 1976

Sit in Easy Pose with a straight spine and a light Neck Lock.

Mudra: Interlace your fingers with your right thumb on top. Place your hands at the center of your diaphragm line, touching your body. Maintain the shoulders completely relaxed. You should have pressure at your hands but none at your shoulders.

Eye Focus: Closed.

Breath: Concentrate on your breath at the Tip of the Nose. Be aware of which nostril you are breathing through. Within 3 minutes, you should know. Then change it. If you are breathing primarily through your left nostril, consciously change to your right nostril.

Time: 11-31 minutes.

Comments: The ability to be aware of and consciously change which nostril is active is a simple and helpful practice that even a young child can learn. Switching the dominant nostril can change your mental state. For example, if you are irritated or depressed, try breathing through the right nostril and see what happens.

Meditation to Remove the Fear of the Future

October 26, 1988

Sit in Easy Pose with a straight spine and a light Neck Lock.

Mudra: Place the left hand in the palm of the right hand. Grasp the left hand by curling right fingers around the left hand and the right thumb on the left palm. Cross the left thumb over the right thumb. Hold this mudra gently on the Heart Center.

Eye Focus: Not specified.

Breath: Not specified.

Mantra: Meditate on your favorite version of the shabd: **DHAN DHAN RAM DAS GUROO**[28].

Time: Start with **11 minutes** and slowly build to **31 minutes**.

To End: Inhale deeply, exhale. Repeat **2 more times**.

Comments: This meditation clears the fear of the future which has been created by your subconscious memories of the past. Without judgment, it connects you to the flow of life and helps you become conscious of the Self through your Heart Center. The mudra at the Heart Center awakens a peaceful, secure feeling.

---

28   This shabd reaches the realm of miracles, where the impossible becomes possible. When life seems stuck, praise the domain of Guru Ram Das, the realm of the true Reality. It is the realm of the heart, of the Neutral Mind, where all things become pure.

Meditation for Anti-Depression and Brain Synchrony

January 23, 1975

PART ONE

Sit in Easy Pose with a straight spine and a light Neck Lock.

Mudra: Place the hands in Gyan Mudra, touch the tip of the thumbs with the Jupiter (index) fingers, and keep the other three fingers extended. Raise the upper arms parallel to the ground and bring the hands in front of the eyes so that the thumbs and Jupiter fingers of each hand touch in front of the bridge of the nose. The palms will face away from the body. On the inhale, moving the forearms, separate the hands 36-45 inches (92-115 cm). Keep the upper arms parallel to the ground. On the exhale, return to the original position. Synchronize the movement, breath and mantra.

Eye Focus: Wide open, staring at the horizon.

Breath: Inhale as the hands separate, exhale as the hands touch in front of the face.

Mantra: SAA TAA NAA MAA. Mentally chant **SAA** on the inhale, **TAA** on the exhale, **NAA** on the inhale, **MAA** on the exhale.

Time: Start with a slow movement of 8 seconds per cycle (**SAA TAA NAA MAA**) for the first **2-3 minutes** and then increase the speed to 3-4 seconds per cycle for **3 more minutes**. Total time: **5-6 minutes**. Gradually increase the time to **11 minutes** as you increase the time in Part Two to 31 minutes.

Comments: Meditate on the life energy of the breath. Feel as though you are stretching the breath from a single point—the mudras touching—outward to the full extension of the mudras.

PART TWO
Remain in Easy Pose.

Mudra: Relax the arms and shoulders. No mudra is required.

Eye Focus: Not specified.

Breath: Not specified.

Mental Focus: If you need a focus, meditate at the Crown Chakra[29] at the top of the head. Concentrate on total relaxation, or on that one square inch of the skull.

Time: 15 minutes. You can slowly increase the time to **31 minutes** as you increase the time in Part One to 11 minutes.

Comments: This meditation focuses on the range of the breath. In the

---

29   The Crown Chakra, the 7th chakra, also known as the 10th Gate or *Sahasrara*, is our link to the universal and infinite consciousness, or God. With our connection to The Source come our belief systems, belief in a higher power, self-knowledge, transcendence, and universal understanding. When the *Sahasrara* is balanced, we seek out deep questions regarding existence, integrate spiritual teachings, have an open mind, and transcend the ego.

continue on next page ☞

subconscious, breath and life are synonymous. The creativity of your existence is unlimited. We can create negative patterns in our thoughts and actions. This meditation will let you measure how positive or negative you are and make you more positive and happy. By meditating this way, the hemispheres of the brain synchronize, and depression can be alleviated.

KRI KUNDALINI RESEARCH INSTITUTE

Meditation for the Negative Mind

Originally published in The Mind

Sit in Easy Pose with a straight spine and a light Neck Lock.

Mudra: With the arms relaxed at the sides, bend the forearms and bring the hands to heart level. Make a cup of the two hands with the right on top of the left hand. The fingers will cross over each other.

Eye Focus: Slightly open, looking down toward the hands.

Breath: Inhale deeply in a long steady stroke through the nose. Exhale in a focused stream through rounded lips. Feel the breath go into the hands. Let any thought or desire that is negative come into your mind as you breathe. Breathe the thought and feeling in and exhale it out.

Time: 11 to 31 minutes.

To End: Exhale completely and suspend the breath out as you lock in the Navel Point. Concentrate on each vertebra of the spine until you can feel it all the way to the base, as stiff as a rod. Then inhale powerfully, exhale completely, and repeat the concentration. Repeat this final breath **3–5 times**. Relax completely.

Comments: When you need to balance the flashing negativity and protective fervor of the Negative Mind, use this meditation. It clears the subconscious of unwanted negative or fearful thoughts. Then, the Negative Mind can give you clear signals to protect and promote you.

Meditation to Eliminate Inner Conflicts

October 24, 2000

Sit in Easy Pose with a straight spine and a light Neck Lock.

Mudra: Interlace the fingers in Venus Lock and place the hands in front of the Solar Plexus with the palms facing the body.

Eye Focus: Closed.

Breath: Not specified.

Mantra: Chant **HUMEE HUM BRAHM HUM** (The recording by Nirinjan Kaur was played in the original class.)

Time: 22 minutes.

To End: Inhale deeply, suspend the breath for **15 seconds**, exhale. Repeat **2 more times**.

Comments: Listen to the mantra and meditate on the meaning of the words: "We are We, We are God." When you understand this mantra, inner conflict is eliminated.

Meditation to Deepen your Personality

April 24, 2000

Sit in Easy Pose with a straight spine and a light Neck Lock.

Mudra: Stretch the left arm up straight with the palms facing forward and fingers straight and wide apart. There is no bend in the elbow. Make a fist of the right hand with the Jupiter (index) finger extended and the other fingers held down with the thumb. Relax the right elbow at the side of the body and raise the forearm perpendicular to the ground with the right hand at the level of the shoulder, facing forward. Keeping the wrist straight and elbow in place, move the right forearm like a pendulum into the center of the body and back to the starting position, in rhythm with the mantra. On **HAR, HAREE** and **HAY**, the hand moves inward, and on **HARAY, WHAA** and **GUROO**, the hand returns to the starting position.

Eye Focus: Tip of the Nose.

Breath: Not specified.

Mantra: Chant with the tip of the tongue **HAR HARAY HAREE WHAA-HAY GUROO**[30].

Time: 10 minutes.

To End: Inhale deeply, suspend the breath for **15 seconds**, stretch the spine and the Jupiter (index) finger, exhale. Repeat **2 more times**.

---

30 Har Haray Haree, Wahe Guru means "All aspects of the Creator are Bliss". This mantra uses the primal force of creativity to rid one of obnoxious situations in life and can bring you through any block. It opens up your own creative energy.

Adjust your Electromagnetic Field to Recognize your Psyche

March 13, 1990

PART ONE
Sit in Easy Pose with a straight spine and a light Neck Lock.

Mudra: Interlace the fingers and raise the arms up above the head. Lift the rib cage to open the space between the rib cage and the pelvis. Rotate the body rapidly from the Navel Point in counterclockwise circles. The shoulders remain over the hips and move with the rotation. The neck and head stay stable, and arms hold the balance.

Eye Focus: Not specified.

Breath: Not specified.

Time: 6 minutes.

To End: Maintain the movement throughout the ending. Inhale deeply, suspend the breath for **15 seconds**, exhale completely. Inhale and exhale quickly 2 times. Inhale deeply, suspend the breath for **10 seconds**, exhale. Inhale and exhale quickly. Inhale deeply, suspend the breath for **20 seconds**, exhale completely. Relax for a few minutes.

PART TWO (Ajonee Kriya)
Remain in Easy Pose with a straight spine and a light Neck Lock.

Mudra: Interlace the fingers and

lock them on the back of the head. Stretch the elbows out to the sides with the forearms parallel to the ground. Lean back 30 degrees from vertical and twist from side to side.

Eye Focus: Look at the ceiling.

Breath: Not specified.

Mantra: Chant the mantra **HAR SINGH NAR SINGH**. (The recording by Nirinjan Kaur was played in the original class.)

HAR SINGH NAR SINGH NEEL NAARAAYAN, GUROO SIKH GUROO SINGH HAR HAR GAYAN,

WHAA-HAY GUROO WHAA-HAY GUROO, HAR HAR DHIAYAN, SAAKHAT NINDAK DUSHT MATHAAYAN[51]

Time: 7 minutes.

To End: Maintain the movement throughout the ending. Inhale deeply, suspend the breath for **10 seconds**, exhale. Inhale and exhale quickly. Repeat this sequence **2 more times**.

---

51 This mantra means "God the Protector takes care of the universe. Those who live in God's consciousness and power, chant Har Har. Meditate on Wahe Guru and live in that ecstasy. Those who vibrate God's Name and relate to God, all karmas are cleared". It makes one a conqueror of evil. It works on the evolution of energy and the strength of the masculine energy.

continue on next page ☛

PART THREE

Remain in Easy Pose with a straight spine and a light Neck Lock.

Mudra: Place the thumbs on the mounds at the base of the Mercury (little) fingers. Stretch the arms straight forward, parallel to the ground, with the hands facing down and fingers together pointing forward. Actively stretch the shoulders and arms forward, which will lift the body. There is no movement in the body, only the breath moves.

Eye Focus: Closed.

Breath & Mantra: Inhale in **8 strokes** through the nose, exhale in **8 strokes** through the nose as you mentally chant the mantra **SAA TAA NAA MAA, SAA TAA NAA MAA** (1 syllable per stroke).

Time: 1 ½ minutes.

To End: Inhale deeply, keeping the arms straight, press the palms together with fingers pointing forward, suspend the breath for **20 seconds**, exhale. Do this only once. Relax for a few minutes.

Meditation to Relax and Rejoice

February 19, 1979

Sit in Easy Pose with a straight spine and a light Neck Lock.

Mudra: Relax the elbows at the sides and bring the hands in front of the body. Make a fist of the left hand with the thumb inside. Wrap the right hand around the left fist, placing the right thumb over the base of the left thumb. Relax in this position.

Eye Focus: Tip of the Nose.

Breath: Inhale deeply. Chant the following mantra in a monotone on the exhale.

Mantra: HAREE HAR, HAREE HAR, HAREE HAR, HAREE HAR, HAREE HAR, HAREE HAR, HAREE HAR, HAREE HAR

Time: **11 minutes**. Gradually increase the time to **62 minutes** or even **2 ½ hours**.

Comments: This meditation lets you relax and rejoice. It enables you to understand the contrast between working from your ego and working from your inner Self, from your soul, aligned with the Will of God. Allow time to ground yourself after doing this meditation.

Meditation to Develop Self-Reliance

February 14, 2000

Sit in Easy Pose with a straight spine and a light Neck Lock.

Mudra: Raise the arms to shoulder level and parallel to the ground; the upper arms are angled out slightly and the forearms are forward, so that the hands are about shoulder width apart. The palms are facing down, and the fingers are stiff and wide apart. Move the arms forward and back about 4-5 inches (10-13 cm). It is a rapid motion from the shoulders that shakes the rib cage and spine.

Eye Focus: Closed.

Breath: Not specified.

Mantra: Chant the Guru Gaitri mantra with 4 **HAR**. (In the original class, Nirinjan Kaur's version was played.)
HAR HAR HAR HAR GOBINDAY
HAR HAR HAR HAR MUKUNDAY
HAR HAR HAR HAR UDAARAY
HAR HAR HAR HAR APAARAY
HAR HAR HAR HAR HAREEUNG
HAR HAR HAR HAR KAREEUNG
HAR HAR HAR HAR NIRNAAMAY
HAR HAR HAR HAR AKAAMAY[52]

---

52   This mantra fixes the mind for prosperity and power. It contains the eight facets of Self. Har is the original force of Creativity. The four repetitions of Har give power to all aspects and provide the power to break down the barriers of the past. It converts fear into the determination to use and expand the reserve energy of the Navel Point. It invokes guidance and sustenance; all powers come to serve your true purpose.

Time: 16 ½ minutes.

To End: Inhale deeply, suspend the breath for **10 seconds**, straighten and tighten your fingers as much as possible, the hands automatically shake from the force of it. Exhale with Cannon Breath. Repeat **2 more times**.

Comments: Regular practice of this exercise will totally change the psychic flow of your body. You will be different. Your body will receive energy from the universal energy, which is called Prakirti. And as a Purusha and Purkha, you will just blossom. The body is given to you as a gift for you to emit and remit the light of your soul. And when it emits and remits the soul, the universe brings to you what you need. You have only one thing — your breath. You will know who you are if you know the length and strength of your breath. When your mind does not stop and you go crazy, just suspend the breath. When you inhale and suspend it in, the mind comes into balance. When you exhale and suspend it out, your mind becomes intuitive.

WORKING ON
THE SPIRITUAL

"BUOYED BY THE SPIRIT OF THEIR ANCESTORS,
THEY DUG DEEP WITHIN THEMSELVES TO FORGE
A LINK BETWEEN THE AFRICAN SPIRITUALITY
OF THEIR PAST AND THE AFRICAN AMERICAN
SPIRITUALITY THAT WAS COMING TO BIRTH."
PROFESSOR DIANA L. HAYES, AUTHOR

It would not be inaccurate to say that spirituality is in the bones of those of African descent. Spirituality allows us the peace, love, strength, and foundation to feel and know our soul, as well as our connection to one another and the divine. We have survived the Maafa, the atrocities done against enslaved Africans, because of a strong relationship with the One. Holding on to traditional ways of connecting with the Divine and adapting have been essential to our survival.

Unfortunately, too many of us believe that we are alone with our stress and frustrations, anger and depression, discontent, and despair. When we most need our spirituality, many of us are cut off from it for a number of reasons.

Rekindling connection with your soul and the divine is the hallmark of a Kundalini Yoga and meditation practice. It allows us to take our own lived experiences and transform our perception of ourselves, the way we see the world, and, ultimately, reality. As our African ancestors knew, it is within us that we must look in order to affect our situations and conditions. This is achievable because we are one with all that exists.

Healing the Physical, Mental and Spiritual Bodies

February 1, 1995

Sit in Easy Pose with a straight spine and a light Neck Lock.

Mudra: Split the fingers of each hand so that the Sun (ring) and Mercury (little) fingers are together and the Jupiter (index) and Saturn (middle) fingers are together, thumbs relaxed. Stretch the left arm out to the side, parallel to the ground, with the palm facing down. Stretch the right arm up straight with the palm facing forward. There is no bend in the elbows.

Eye Focus: Closed.

Breath: Not specified.

Mantra: If you wish to use a mantra with this meditation, you may use **HAR HARAY HAREE WHAA-HAY GUROO**[33]. You may chant it aloud, mentally chant it, or listen to it. It is your choice.

Time: 11 minutes (maximum).

To End: Inhale deeply, suspend the breath for **10 seconds**, stretch and tighten your entire body, exhale. Repeat **2 more times**.

Comments: This meditation promotes powerful self-purification. The posture will hurt as long as you have

---

33   This is a shakti mantra plus a bhakti mantra. It expresses the three qualities of the word Har, the Creative Infinity: seed, flow, completion, unto the Infinite. This mantra can bring you through any block in life.

any toxins in your body. The arms must be stretched from the armpits with no bend in the elbows. It can give you complete control of your being, increase intuition and improve your health. Releasing all garbage: physical, mental, and spiritual.

To practice this meditation for 40 days, alternate the arm position each day. The first day, practice with the right arm up and the left arm out to the side. The next day, practice with the left arm up and the right arm out to the side, and so on. After 40 days, the meditation will start working on your subtle bodies. Whatever happens after 40 days, keep it to yourself.

Strengthening Intuitive Projection

November 13, 1985

PART ONE

Sit in Easy Pose with a straight spine and a light Neck Lock.

Mudra: Move your arms as if you are swimming. Extend one and then the other in a constant motion. Move vigorously.

Eye Focus: Closed.

Breath: Allow it to naturally adjust with the movement.

Mental Focus: As you swim, imagine yourself in a vast ocean as night is falling and a storm is coming. You can't see the shore, so use your intuition to determine which way to go to reach the shore. Whichever direction your intuition directs you, project yourself in that direction. Imagine that your survival depends on swimming in the right direction. Swim vigorously; the motion will automatically create a specific breathing rhythm.

Time: 11 ½ minutes.
Immediately begin Part Two.

Comments: The breath rhythm achieved through vigorous movement will help you develop your ability to think intuitively.

PART TWO
Sit on the heels in Rock Pose.

Mudra: Bend forward from the hips and place the forehead to the ground so that the Third Eye Point makes contact, relax the hands next to the body with the palms facing up in Baby Pose[34]. Relax the spine.

Eye Focus: Not specified.

34   Baby Pose is a resting posture often done between exercises. It is good for calming. Begin by sitting back on the heels, closing the eyes, then leaning forward and bringing the forehead to the ground. The arms are resting alongside the body with palms facing up or stretched out in front. Baby Pose is good to do every day as it creates an inflow of spinal serum that refreshes the nerves of the spinal column.

Breath: Not specified.

Mental Focus: As your head touches the ground, imagine your relief that you have made it safely to the shore. Feel gratitude in every cell.

Time: 7 minutes.

To End: Inhale deeply and, while still in Baby Pose, move the spine in all directions to loosen and adjust itself. Gradually rise up and relax.

Comments: "Intuitive projection and intuitive reception are your guardian angels." Yogi Bhajan.

Meditation For The Arcline and To Clear The Karmas

August 1, 1996

Sit in Easy Pose with a straight spine and a light Neck Lock.

Mudra: Rest the elbows at the sides of the body. Extend the forearms forward parallel to the ground with hands facing up, slightly cupped. Keeping the elbows bent, raise the arms up and back over the shoulders as far back as possible on each **"WHAA-HAY GUROO"** and **"WHAA-HAY JEEO"**. Immediately return to the starting position (1 cycle per 2 seconds). The movement is as if scooping water and throwing it with a flick of the wrists over the shoulders and through the arcline[35].

Eye Focus: Closed.

Breath: Not specified.

---

35 The arcline is a halo that stretches around your forehead from earlobe to earlobe. It is the nucleus of the aura. Women have an extra arcline that runs from nipple to nipple and assists in the bonding with an infant. The arcline is your projection and radiance. It gives you the ability to focus, to be concentrated, to meditate. It is associated with the pituitary gland and regulates the nervous system and glandular balance, thus protecting your heart center.

Mantra: Listen to the mantra: **WHAA-HAY GUROO, WHAA-HAY GUROO, WHAA-HAY GUROO, WHAA-HAY JEEO**[56] ("Wahe Guru, Wahe Guru, Wahe Guru, Wahe Jio," by Giani Ji, was played in the original class.)

Time: 31 minutes.

To End: Inhale deeply, stretch the hands as far back as possible, suspend the breath for **10-15 seconds**, exhale. Repeat **2 more times**.

Comments: This meditation is said to clear karmic memories that are held within the arcline. The power of Infinity is within you, not outside of you.

56　This mantra is an expression of how great the creator is. It translates as "Wow, God is great!" or "Indescribably great is His Infinite Wisdom." It is also a mantra of ecstasy. "Jeeo" is an affectionate but respectful variation of the word "Jee", which means soul. The word "Jeeo" sends the message directly to the soul. "O my soul, God is!" Chanting this mantra creates a very subtle rub against the center of the upper palate and stimulates the meridian known in the West as the Christ Meridian Point and in the East as Sattvica Buddha Bindu.

See Your Soul Through the Third Eye

June 23, 1989

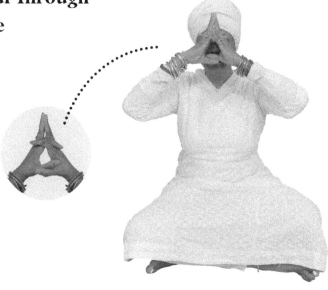

Sit in Easy Pose with a straight spine and apply a light Neck Lock.

Mudra & Mantra: Start by interlacing the fingers. Extend the little, ring, and middle fingers so they point straight up. Separate the base of the palms about 4 inches (10 cm) so the three fingers form a teepee and there is a round space between the index fingers and thumbs. Raise this mudra up and put your nose in the opening between the index fingers and the thumbs. Chant the mantra:

**HAR HAR GOBINDAY,
HAR HAR MUKANDAY,
HAR HAR UDAARAY,
HAR HAR APAARAY,**

**HAR HAR HAREEUNG,
HAR HAR KAREEUNG,
HAR HAR NIRNAAMAY,
HAR HAR AKAAMAY.**

Meditation: As you chant, firmly press the tips of the three fingers in sequence. Begin with the middle fingertips on the first **HAR,** then the ring fingertips on the next **HAR,** and finally the little fingertips on **GOBINDAY**. Reverse the order for the next line. Continue reversing the order with each line as you move along the 8 lines.

Eye Focus: Third Eye Point.

Time: Continue for **11 to 31 minutes**.

To End: Inhale deeply, suspend, and focus at the Third Eye Point. Then exhale powerfully through the mouth. Repeat **2 more times**, and relax.

Comments: The Jupiter (index) fingers represent the guru and the thumbs the ego, the id; thus, in this mudra, the guru sits over the ego. The thumbs put a little pressure on the nostrils where the Ida and Pingala nadis end. The Jupiter fingers activate the Third Eye. We only see reflections with our physical eyes; it is the Third Eye that truly sees.

Meditation for Guidance

July 11, 1986

Sit in Easy Pose with a straight spine and a light Neck Lock.

Mudra: Raise the arms in front of the body and place the right forearm on top of the left, parallel to the ground. Rest the forearms against the body with the left hand holding the forearm below the right elbow, and the right hand in a fist nestled inside the left elbow. On each stroke of the inhale, expand the chest and lift the locked arms upward, just off the body, and back down. On the exhale, the arms remain still in the original position. Move very gently up and down with the inbreath.

Eye Focus: Closed.

Breath: Inhale in **8 strokes** through the nose, exhale completely in **1 stroke** through the nose.

Mantra: Meditate on the mantra **RAKHAY RAKHANHAAR.**[37]

---

37 These are the words of Guru Arjan, the 5th Sikh Guru, for complete protection. It is from the evening prayer, which adds energy to one's being and helps when you are physically weak or have limited wealth. It is a victory song that allows us to be guided by God's graceful and merciful hand. It does away with the obstacles to fulfilling one's destiny. The translation of the mantra is as follows: "You, Yourself are caring for us all and taking us across, Uplifting and giving us excellence. You gave us the touch of the lotus feet of the Guru, and all our affairs are covered. You are merciful, kind, compassionate; and our minds never forget You. In the company of conscious people, you save us from misfortune. You remove any enemies from our path. You are my anchor. Nanak, keep firm in your mind, by meditating and repeating His Name, I feel peaceful and happy and all my pain departs."

(The recording by Singh Kaur was
played in the original class.)

**RAKHAY RAKHANHAAR
AAP UBAARIUN
GUR KEE PAIREE PAA-
EH KAAJ SAVAARIUN
HOAA AAP DAYAAL
MANHO NA VISAARIUN
SAADH JANAA KAI SUNG
BHAVJAL TAARIUN
SAAKAT NINDAK DUSHT
KHIN MAA-EH BIDAARIUN
TIS SAAHIB KEE TAYK
NAANAK MANAI MAA-EH
JIS SIMRAT SUKH HO-EH
SAGLAY DOOKH JAA-EH**

Time: 31 minutes.

Meditation to Bless Yourself

December 7, 1997

Sit in Easy Pose with a straight spine and a light Neck Lock.

Mudra: Place the left hand on the Heart Center. Raise the right arm in an arc with the right hand 4-6 inches (10-15cm) above the Crown Chakra, the top of the head. The fingers are together and palm facing down.

Eye Focus: Closed.

Mantra: Chant aloud, using the tip of your tongue: **ONG NAMO GUROO DAYV NAMO.**

Mental Focus: Become calm, and with the mantra, project yourself into the vastness of Infinity. Feel that it is the God within you that is chanting. Drop all limitations.

Time: 11 minutes.

To End: Inhale deeply, suspend the breath for **15 seconds**, squeeze the body tight, and exhale with Cannon Breath. Repeat **2 more times**. Relax.

Comments: Blessing yourself is a communication with the higher Self. It accepts that everything is part of the One and that we have a right to bless. It is an act of self-dignity and humility. To bless, the ego has to be less. We often neglect self-blessing, which is not to satisfy the ego but rather self-care. Blessings and prayers are closely related. Both require a communication or creation of a common notion. Prayers are the common notion of oneness between you and your Unknown. Blessings are the common notion of elevation and expansion between every finite part of your life and your unlimited self.

"It is the first human right and duty to bless the self and to bless all. It is a function of the spirit, as fragrance is the nature of the rose," Yogi Bhajan. He also said that "blessed are those who bless themselves. Pure are those who purify themselves".

Ashtang Agni Kriya – The Eightfold Spiritual Fire Kriya

July 24, 1996

Sit in Easy Pose with a straight spine and a light Neck Lock.

Mudra: Raise the elbows out to the sides and up to shoulder level. The hands are an extension of the arms, with no bend in the wrists. Forcefully bring the upper arms and elbows down to hit the ribs on the sides of the body. Immediately return to the starting position. The movement is rapid and continuous, in rhythm with the music. When the elbows hit the body, the breath is automatically exhaled. Let the entire body above the Navel Center dance with the movement.

Eye Focus: Not specified.

Breath: It will become Breath of Fire as you practice.

Mantra: Listen to the mantra **GOBINDE MUKANDAY** (A version by Matamandir Singh was played in the original class).

Time: 6 minutes, rest for **2 minutes** and continue for **5 more minutes. Total Time: 11 minutes.** Slowly increase the time to 15 minutes maximum.

Comments: The movement can be practiced moderately and rhythmically and, over time, worked up to Breath of Fire speed. Make the rib cage into a drum by stretching the spine and lifting the chest, holding the ribs slightly expanded to create a solid surface that the upper arms beat. "The kriya will develop the fire energy that is our God within us: pure, powerful and all-prevailing, with which we shall burn the karma." Yogi Bhajan

Meditation for Rasa and the Inner Eye

January 5, 1995

Sit in Easy Pose with a straight spine and a light Neck Lock.

Mudra: Place the center of the left palm on the Navel Point, with the fingers pointing towards the right. Raise the right hand above the head a few inches from the hairline, palm down. (It is in line with the arcline that circles from ear to ear.) Move the hand rapidly in synchrony with the mantra. The hand moves a few inches (7–15 cm) in a fast, staccato pulse.

Eye Focus: Third Eye Point.

Mental Focus: Imagine the energy released from the Navel Point and trace its path along the spine through the head to the forehead and Tip of the Nose. Sense the temperature and sensations in the palm of the left hand. The exercise can create heat.

Mantra: Chant **HAR** approximately 3 times per second. Create a continuous sound current, focus on the mantra, and project it.

Time: 11 minutes.

To End: Inhale deeply, suspend the breath, keep the right hand fixed over and a few inches (7–15 cm) above the forehead. Focus on the energy between the palm and the head, press on the Navel Point and sense the energy in that area, exhale with Cannon Breath.

KRI KUNDALINI RESEARCH INSTITUTE

Inhale deeply, suspend the breath, and concentrate at the pituitary, squeeze the muscles along the spine, and feel the energy flow like a snake along the spine from the base to the top and over the forehead to the pituitary at the root of the nose. Exhale with Cannon Breath. Repeat the last breath and meditative projection **1 more time.** Relax for a minute or two, then repeat the meditation for **11 more minutes.**

Comments: The fast vibration of the right hand keeps you focused and energizes the arcline and the aura. Har is chanted with the Navel Point and tip of the tongue. This is the sound of creativity, the creative power of consciousness. Be aware; speak and listen as you speak. Hear the inner sound of the sound. Sense the shift in your energetic bodies as the sounds prepare to arise and manifest on your tongue and through your chakras. As you continue, the pressure on your nerves will increase greatly. You are reshaping your central nervous system.

Reaching a Stress-Free Zone in Our Own Self

March 23, 1990

PART ONE
Sit in Easy Pose with a straight spine and a light Neck Lock.

Mudra: Press the tip of the tongue upward on the membrane between the upper lip and gum. At the same time, pull down on the upper lip, creating a resistance between the opposing forces; it will be painful. Place the hands on the knees with no bend in the elbows. Hands are in Ravi Mudra, the tips of the thumbs and Sun (ring) fingers touching, with the other fingers straight.

Eye Focus: Tip of the Nose.

Breath: Not specified.

Mental Focus: Sense as if you are above the body as high as the ceiling. This increases the healing effect.

Time: 15 minutes. (Gong was played in the original class, including during the ending.)

To End: Inhale deeply, suspend the breath for **20 seconds**, press the tongue up and tighten the body, exhale. Repeat **2 more times**. Immediately start Part Two.

Comments: This exercise is called Dukhnaasini Kriya, which can take away disease and discomfort. Allow yourself to sweat.

PART TWO
Remain in Easy Pose.

Mudra: Keep the tongue in the same position as part One. Interlock the hands in Venus Lock and stretch the arms up above the head, elbows are slightly bent. Rotate the upper body into counterclockwise circles. Use the power of the arms, not the lower body, to create the movement.

Eye Focus: Tip of the Nose.

Breath: Not specified.

Mantra: Listen to Pran Bandha Mantra. ("Pavan Guru," by Guru Shabad Singh Khalsa, was played in the original class.)

PAVAN PAVAN PAVAN PAVAN
PAR PARAA PAVAN GUROO
PAVAN GUROO WHAA-
HAY GUROO
WHAA-HAY GUROO
PAVAN GUROO[58]

Time: 9 minutes.

To End: Inhale deeply, suspend the breath for **20 seconds**, lift the rib cage, stretch the spine, exhale. Repeat **2 more times**.

---

58   Pavan is the air, the breath, carrier of the praana, the life force. This is the Divine in action. This mantra increases the pranic energy and gives the experience of "may the force be with you."

continue on next page ☞

Comments: Sweat and expel toxins and disease from the body. "The first step to enjoy life is to share your talent. The second step is to share your courage. The third is to share your grace, wisdom, tranquility. Finally, share your nobility. You will find yourself fulfilled," Yogi Bhajan.

Experience the Source of Your Infinity

April 15, 2000

PART ONE
Sit in Easy Pose with a straight spine and a light Neck Lock.

Mudra: Place the hands in Gyan Mudra, touch the tips of the thumbs and the Jupiter (index) fingers, and keep the other three fingers extended and spread apart. Stretch the arms straight forward parallel to the ground with the palms facing down and fingers pointing forward.

Breath: Not specified.

Eye Focus: Tip of the Nose.

Mantra: WHAA-HAY GUROO, WHAA-HAY GUROO, WHAA-HAY GUROO, WHAA-HAY JEEO

Chant with the tip of the tongue and pull the navel with each **WHAA-HAY**. (Sangeet Kaur and Harjinder Singh's version, from Raga Sadhana, was played in the original class.)

Time: 11 minutes. Immediately begin Part Two.

Comments: Do not bend the elbows and keep the arms parallel to the ground to maintain the balance of the magnetic field.

continue on next page ☞

PART TWO
Remain in Easy Pose.

Mudra: Firmly press the hands on the Heart Center.

Eye Focus: Tip of the Nose.

Breath: Not specified.

Mantra: WHAA-HAY GUROO, WHAA-HAY GUROO, WHAA-HAY GUROO, WHAA-HAY JEEO
Continue chanting the mantra for **2 ½ minutes**. Whisper powerfully for **2 more minutes**.

Total time: 4 ½ minutes.
Immediately begin Part Three.

PART THREE
Remain in Easy Pose.

Mudra: Press firmly on the Navel Point with both hands.

Eye Focus: Tip of the Nose.

Mantra: WHAA-HAY GUROO, WHAA-HAY GUROO, WHAA-HAY GUROO, WHAA-HAY JEEO

a) Whisper strongly for **1 ½ minutes**.
b) Inhale and exhale strongly through the mouth for **2 ½ minutes**.
c) Whistle loudly for **1 ½ minutes**.

To End: Inhale deeply, suspend the breath for **10 seconds**, exhale with Cannon Breath. Repeat 1 more time. Inhale and relax.

Comments: Using the tip of the tongue to chant stimulates the meridian points in the palate connected to the hypothalamus and thalamus. They communicate with the pituitary to affect the rest of the glandular system. In a few minutes, the entire body changes.

"If God has created you and if He has created me, then let us relax. He is a Creator: believe it, trust it and understand it with the purity of your heart. Your inner purity and intuitiveness must know whether something is right for you or not. Meditation and mantra will give you intuition so you do not have to live by impulse," Yogi Bhajan.

Merging with Infinity Meditation

February 11, 1998

PART ONE
Sit in Easy Pose with a straight spine and a light Neck Lock.

Mudra: Stretch the arms forward parallel to the ground with the palms pressed together, fingers pointing forward, and the right thumb over the left. Keep the elbows straight and bring the elbows together as close as possible.

Eye Focus: Closed.

Breath: Not specified.

Mantra: Whistle with the music (the instrumental version of Ardas Bhaee from the album Healing Sounds of the Ancients #5 was played in the original class).

Time: 11 minutes. Immediately begin Part Two.

PART TWO
Remain in Easy Pose.

Mudra: Raise the arms out to the sides and up about 45 degrees from parallel. The hands extend with no bend in the wrists and are relaxed and open.

Eye Focus: Not specified.

Breath: Breath of Fire.

Time: 1 minute. Immediately begin Part Three.

PART THREE
Remain in Easy Pose.

Mudra: Relax the hands in the lap with interlaced fingers. Become thoughtless.

Eye Focus: Closed.

Breath: Not specified.

Time: 3 minutes.

To End: Inhale deeply, suspend the breath for **15 seconds**, press the tongue on the upper palate, exhale. Repeat **2 more times**.

Meditation on the Divine Law

January 6, 1977

Sit with a straight spine and a light Neck Lock. Place the right heel on the left thigh, close to the left hip.

Mudra: Cross the forearms in front, with the right arm closer to the body. Bend the left hand so that the palm faces up and the fingers point to the left. Bring the right hand, palm up, under the left hand, and fold the right fingers over the outer (Mercury little finger) side of the left hand. The right thumb is relaxed. The base of the left hand will be a few inches below the chin.

Eye Focus: 1/10th open.

Breath: Normal.

Mantra: Meditate on any mantra you choose.

Time: Start slowly and work up to **31 minutes**.

KRI KUNDALINI RESEARCH INSTITUTE

DEVELOPING NEW HABITS

How to Rewire Your Brain and Overcome the Looping Mind

The looping mind is one that returns a person to the same old ways of acting, feeling, and thinking, despite best efforts to counteract that. A few examples:

» You and a sibling are having a disagreement. Frustrated, you bring up an incident that occurred years ago that casts your sibling in a negative light. Your sibling returns that barb with something that brings up negative emotions for you. You two do this all the time, causing each other emotional turmoil. Afterward, you always vow not to let your mind and mouth go there. Unfortunately, the next time you meet, it'll be the same thing. Both of you suffer from habitual negative thought patterns and behaviors.

» It is rare that you share because you often think that you don't have enough. When you do think you have enough to share, you end up not sharing because you think you need to save for a time when you won't have enough. You often think that there is not enough. You think in terms of lack.

» You feel less than. You look at others and think that they are somehow "better" than you. When you see or hear of someone you know progressing in some way, you have something negative to say about it. You have feelings in the back of your mind that you do not deserve the happiness that you perceive others to have. At times, you are depressed about this situation as well. Generally, you are insecure.

» You check your social media accounts constantly. You think and feel that you must. You feel you must respond or see how others are responding to you on social media. You do this even though, when you look up, time has passed, and you find that you're going to be late for work as a result. You didn't hear what your child, whom you're supposed to be helping with last-minute homework, just said to you because you were on one of your devices. You're addicted to your devices.

Habitual thoughts and behaviors are not you. You are divine, created in the image of the indwelling One, the Creator of all, the great I Am. If you want to change your life, you must address the negative thoughts that lurk in your subconscious mind. You must break the cycle of negative thoughts, feelings, and actions. Habits are formed based on past experiences. They become automatic and steeped in our subconscious. Yogi Bhajan said that 60 to 85% of our behavior is based on habits. "First you make habits, then habits make you. It's a very old saying."[39]

Habits are either good or bad for you, depending on whether they promote and support you or whether they move you away for your highest good. What negative habit would you like to break? According to yogic technology, it takes 40 days to establish a promoting habit, 90 days to confirm it, and 120 days for the good habit to be embedded in your psyche. Regular practice helps to break habits that block and bind us and create new habits that promote and support us. The practices of Kundalini Yoga—breathwork, kriyas, meditations, mudras, and eye focus—work synergistically to positively re-pattern the brain. Below[40] is the special technology Yogi Bhajan shared with us relating to the breaking of negative habits that are a result of the looping mind.

11 days: 11 is the number of Infinity in the material world and the conqueror of the physical realm.
So, it's like the first step to breaking free from the entanglement of the mind.

40 days: It takes 40 days to break a habit. Forty days helps break negative habits that block you from the expansion possible through the kriya or mantra, if done 40 days straight in a row.

90 days: It takes 90 days to confirm a habit. When you practice a kriya or mantra for 90 days straight, it will establish a new habit in your conscious and subconscious minds. It will change you in a very deep way.

120 days: The new habit is who you are. When you commit to practicing a kriya or mantra for 120 days without skipping a day, it will confirm the new habit of consciousness. The positive effects of a kriya, meditation, or mantra become permanently ingrained in your mind.

1000 days: You have mastered the new habit. This will allow you to master the

---

39   The Library of Teachings, November 20, 1973

40   The Aquarian Teacher Level One Textbook, 2020, page 148.

new habit of consciousness that a kriya, meditation, or mantra has promised. No matter what the challenge, you can call on this new habit to serve you.

Know that a habit is a subconscious chain reaction between the mind, the glandular system, and the nervous system. We develop habits at a very young age. Some of them serve our highest destiny, some of them do not. By doing a 40-, 90-, 120-, or 1000-day sadhana[41] (daily practice), you can rewire that chain reaction. You can develop new, deeply ingrained habits that serve your highest good.

"One part of sadhana should stay constant long enough for you to master it, or at least experience the changes evoked by a single technique. Each kriya and mantra has its individual effects, although they all elevate you toward a cosmic consciousness. Learn to value the pricelessness of one kriya, and all others will be understood in a clearer light."[42]

Another way Kundalini Yoga can rewire your brain is to practice meditation for an extended period of time. The amount of time affects the body, the mind, and the spirit in different ways. See below how the effects of Kundalini Yoga change with time.

3 minutes: Affects the electromagnetic field, circulation, and chemistry of the blood. The increased blood circulation begins distributing enhanced neuroendocrine secretions throughout the body.

7 minutes: Brain patterns begin to change from the static of beta waves to calmer alpha waves and, eventually, deep relaxing delta waves. Simultaneously, the magnetic force surrounding the body increases in strength.

11 minutes: The pituitary gland, the glandular system, and the nerves start to learn and change. The sympathetic and parasympathetic nervous systems begin to accommodate the increased energy.

---

41 "Sadhana means a given time and space in which you practice a technology to enhance your spirit." Yogi Bhajan, 5/25/78. One part of sadhana should stay constant long enough for you to master, or at least experience, the changes evoked by a single technique. Each kriya and mantra has its individual effects, although they all elevate you toward a cosmic consciousness. Learn to value the pricelessness of one kriya, and all others will be understood in a clearer light.

42 The Aquarian Teacher, Level One Textbook, 2020, page 148.

22 minutes: Anxiety-producing thoughts in the subconscious begin to clear. Your three minds (negative, positive, and neutral) start to work together, so your mental integration changes. 22 is the infinite number of longing and gives mastery of the mental realm.

31 minutes: The glands, breath, and concentration affect all the cells and rhythms of the body. Endocrinological balance is achieved, as is the balance of the chakras of the ethereal body, such as the aura. This balance persists throughout the day and is reflected by changes in mood and behavior.

62 minutes: It changes the gray matter in the brain. The subconscious "shadow mind" and the outer projection are integrated.
2 ½ hours: It alters the psyche's co-creation with the surrounding magnetic field, causing the subconscious mind to be firmly held in the new pattern by the surrounding universal mind.

Eat to Live—A Form of Self-Love

Quite simply, if you want a healthy body, you must fuel it with healthy food. With healthy food, you get a healthy mind, a healthy body, and a healthy spirit. The sodas, the chips, the processed, fried and fast foods are literally killing us. What are some alternatives?

Start by changing the ways in which you prepare food. Bake instead of frying. Steam your vegetables rather than overcook them in water. Cut down on meat (this includes red meat, poultry, and fish). Instead of consuming it every day, choose to eat it three times a week instead, for example. Drink a lot more water to help flush out your overworked kidneys. Next, buy organic and non-GMO foods.

GOING ORGANIC

The organic movement began in the 1940s, when it was learned that farmers were using more and more pesticides on crops. When researching data on the harmful effects of pesticides, scientists look at farm workers as their barometer or test cases, as farmers are out there in the trenches—literally. Consumer Reports lists 13 known pesticide hazards to humans[45]. These include

---

43   *From Crop to Table.* Consumer Reports. Retrieved March 6, 2019 from https://article.images.consumerreports. org/prod/content/dam/cro/news_articles/health/CR_F SASC_FromCroptoTablePesticides_Mar2015.pdf

ADHD, low IQ in children, Alzheimer's disease, birth defects, depression, breast cancer, immune system damage, fertility issues, ovarian cancer, breast cancer, prostate cancer, Parkinson's disease, and respiratory problems.

As awareness of the use of pesticides harmful to humans has grown, so, too, have consumer purchases of all things organic. However, some people buy fewer organic products than they would like due to perceived expense or because they live in a food desert, where healthy selections, including organic choices, are few. Expenses also present challenges for lower-income earners who would like to buy organic. More labor, time to grow, crop rotation, and demand are some of the reasons given for the expense of organic foods.

ALTERNATIVES?

Be selective in your organic choices. The following foods are listed as having the highest pesticide content. At the very least, purchase organic versions of foods such as strawberries, apples, nectarines, peaches, celery, grapes, cherries, spinach, tomatoes, red peppers, cherry tomatoes, cucumbers, hot peppers, kale, green beans, and collard greens. The list changes from year to year. Be proactive. Wash your fruit and vegetables well, even if they are organic[44]. Use a little Dr. Bronner's peppermint soap diluted with water.

You can also grow your own food. Even apartment dwellers can grow their own food. Get 10-gallon buckets, drill holes in the bottom, get organic soil, purchase organic, non-GMO seeds, and place your buckets in a sunny area. You can grow things like cucumbers, okra, dandelions, greens, wild arugula, kale, lettuce greens, callaloo, scallions, microgreens, ginger, cherry and plum tomatoes, onions, zucchinis, all manner of herbs—and much more! You can even grow yams in a bucket![45]

---

44   See *Organic Foods: Are they safer? More nutritious?* The Mayo Clinic. Retrieved March 6, 2019 from https://www.mayoclinic.org/healthy-lifestyle/nutrition-and-healthy-eating/in-depth/organic-food/art-20043880

45   If you have even a small patio or balcony, check Maggie Stuckey and Rose Marie Nichols McGee book *McGee & Stuckey's Bountiful Container: Create Container Gardens of Vegetables, Herbs, Fruits, and Edible Flowers.* Workman Publishing Company, 2002. Also check "5 Tips How to Grow a Ton of Sweet Potato in One Container or Garden Bed" https://www.youtube.com/watch?v=lbcIrnEfbcM. For full details on growing your own sweet potato slips indoors, see https://www.youtube.com/watch?v=3HrbODzYLy0atch?v=lbcIrnEfbcM. For tips on growing and rooting sweet potatoes indoors, see https://www.youtube.com/watch?v=RWx6epbIDQA

SOME WORDS ABOUT SOY

Some time ago, I was doing some administrative work for Queen Afua, the holistic health practitioner, wellness coach, and pioneer in the green foods movement. She was walking through the office when she looked at my face and asked, "Have you been eating a lot of soy?" It just so happened that I had been consuming quite a bit of soy in the form of various soy "meats," from soy chicken to soy burgers, and soy milk as well. I had noticed a change in my complexion—a discoloration with some almost imperceptible vertical lines on my cheeks. As soon as I gave up the soy, the skin condition cleared.

The isoflavones present in soy mimic estrogen, which has been shown to cause hormonal imbalance. Many people consider it to be pro-inflammatory, and the American Nutrition Association claims that it also appears to contribute to autoimmune thyroid disease, cardiomyopathy, and cardiac rhythm issues. It includes phytates, which reduce the body's capacity to absorb minerals, particularly zinc. It's also high in oxalates, which can cause kidney stones in certain people. Soy also includes natural protease inhibitors, and protease inhibitors hinder your capacity to digest and absorb important nutrients from soy and other meals consumed concurrently. According to a 2005 study by Dr. Kaayla T. Daniel, epidemiological, clinical and laboratory studies link soy to malnutrition, digestive problems, thyroid dysfunction, cognitive decline, reproductive disorders, heart disease and cancer.[46]

A National Institute of Environmental Health Sciences (NIEHS) study found that when comparing newborns fed soy formula to infants fed cow-milk formula, soy formula females had bigger wombs and vaginal cell alterations. According to the researchers, these tissues are susceptible to estrogen-like chemicals present in soy. Alarming fact: seventy percent of the babies in the study were African Americans.[47]

46   Kaayla T Daniel.The Whole Soy Story: The Dark Side of America's Favorite Health Food. Newtrends Publishing, Inc.: 2005.

47   "Soy Infant Formula". National Institute of Environmental Health Sciences. Retrieved March 6, 2019 from https://www.niehs.nih.gov/health/topics/agents/sya-soy-formula/index.cfm
"Babies fed soy-based formula have changes in reproductive system tissues". Science Daily. Retrieved March 6, 2019 from https://www.sciencedaily.com/releases/2018/03/180312150509.htm

There is just too long a list of negatives where soy is concerned—mainly because, here in the West, it is overconsumed and overprocessed[48]. You may want to leave soy alone too, unless it's fermented like tempeh, which has a high protein content, is good for the gut, and has other benefits. Even then, everything is in moderation.

WHY SHOULD YOU GO ORGANIC AND WHAT IS GMO?

Studies show that organic food has a higher nutritional value. Organic produce has been grown in soil that contains no synthetic fertilizers or harmful pesticides[49]. The crops grown in organic soil are rotated so that it remains nutrient-rich.

GMO stands for "genetically modified organism" and is also referred to as "genetically engineered", GE, or "genetically modified", GM. Genetic modification involves gene splicing. GMOs are organisms whose genetic material has been altered by genetic engineering techniques that do not otherwise occur in nature, rather than by traditional cross-breeding and hybridization.

For example, genes from different species can be combined to create fruits and vegetables that are more resistant to certain external factors such as herbicides, fungi, and pests or that have other purported benefits over their natural counterparts. Though on the surface this may sound like a positive thing, the truth is that, at the time of this writing, there have been no long-term studies to determine the effect of GMO food on the human body. The closest we have are very telling statistics involving the high rate of cancer and other illnesses suffered by farm workers[50].

Bottom line, when it comes to your food, stay as close to nature as possible. The further away from nature you stray, the more your mind and body will physically pay. Wherever and however possible, eat green, drink green and live green.

---

48   For more detailed information, see "Studies Showing Adverse Effects of Dietary Soy". Weston A. Price Foundation. Retrieved March 6, 2019 from https://www.westonaprice.org/health-topics/soy-alert/studies-showing-adverse-effects-of-dietary-soy-1939-2008/ Also check Dr. Llaila Afrika, Open Your Mind 101 Conversations. Retrieved March 6, 2019 from https://steemit.com/health/@mcnattydread/dr-llaila-afrika-exposes-truth-on-soy-salt-and-sugars-or-details-of-bad-and-good-foods

49   Exposed and Ignored: How Pesticides are Endangering Our Nations' Farmworkers. A Report by Farmworker Justice. Retrieved June 19, 2019 from https://www.farmworkerjustice.org/sites/default/files/aExposed%20and%20Ignored%20by%20Farmworker%20Justice%20singles%20compressed.pdf

50   For more, see Human Health Effects of Genetically Engineered Crops. Retrieved June 19, 2019 from https://www.ncbi.nlm.nih.gov/books/NBK424554/ and GMOs—Top Five Concerns for Family Farmers. Retrieved June 19, 2019 from https://www.farmaid.org/issues/gmos/gmos-top-5-concerns-for-family-farmers/

ACKNOWLEDGEMENTS

—

To my grandbabies, Jayla and Anala, and my future grandbabies, may you always know the love of self, the indwelling God, and that of family. I send you love through time and space. To my mother, Oreatha Mahone, whose endurance, perseverance, and creativity I admire and embrace, I'm glad I chose you and Daddy. To my children, Jorel and Kenya, and my siblings, Ronald, Grandal, Brenda, and Jennelle: love you and thank you for the experiences.

Giving thanks to Siri Singh Sahib Bhai Sahib Harbhajan Singh Khalsa Yogiji (Yogi Bhajan), who brought the technology of Kundalini Yoga and White Tantric Yoga to the West from India. Hardly a day goes by without me saying aloud to the master teacher, "Thank you." Thank you for this gift of Kundalini Yoga and meditation. Your sacred gift has guided and sustained me through many challenges, with an overall inner understanding that life is good. I am grateful.

Giving thanks as well to Krisha Kaur of the Tenth Gate in Los Angeles. Master Kundalini Yoga teacher, my example, my inspiration—tough but loving— you gave me a wealth of priceless knowledge, opportunities and encouragement. I stand on your shoulders.

A special thank you to Siri Neel Khalsa and Maya Breuer, who both said yes in different ways.

ABOUT THE AUTHOR

—

MutShat Shemsut-Gianprem Kaur took her first Kundalini Yoga class in 1999 after reading Muata Ashby's book *Egyptian Yoga: The Philosophy of Enlightenment*, which talked a lot about the rising of kundalini energy as a way to higher consciousness. At first, her attendance was sporadic. The fallout of a divorce, which was traumatic for all involved, prompted a more serious practice of Kundalini Yoga in 2000. She realized that the practice addressed every human emotion or commotion that one could name, and she saw her way of thinking—and living—shifting in noticeable, positive ways, little by little. Often the only one or sometimes one of a few people of color in her yoga classes, she lamented the fact that those of the African diaspora were missing out on an opportunity to experience the expansiveness and healing that a Kundalini Yoga practice offers.

Then she met Krishna Kaur, a dynamic African-American woman who had studied with the master of Kundalini Yoga himself, Yogi Bhajan. Krishna convinced her to become a certified teacher of Kundalini Yoga. To achieve this, MutShat Shemsut-Gianprem flew from New York to Krishna's teacher training in Los Angeles every month for eight months, becoming a Level One certified Kundalini Yoga instructor in 2008. In addition to Krishna, she has studied with Gurucharan Singh Khalsa and Nirvair Singh Khalsa in Espanola, New Mexico; with Sat Jivan Singh and Sat Jivan Kaur in New York; and with Mehtaband Siri Bahadur in Austin, Texas.

Graduating from Spelman College in 1978 with a B.A. in English, MutShat went on to earn an M.A. in Afro-American studies and an M.S. in journalism from Boston University. She earned an M.S. in Education from Lehman College and an M.S. in School Leadership from Mercy College. She worked as a journalist for a small Harlem newspaper as a teen, then briefly worked as a journalist for a large metropolitan newspaper as an adult. She got married, had children, became a public school teacher, went into work early, left late, paid bills, and knew that there was something else that she should be doing.

As the owner of Purest Light Wellness, a holistic well-being center in the Bronx, New York, she is now doing her mission: helping others on their spiritual journeys while continuing her own. In addition to teaching Kundalini Yoga and Meditation at Level Two, she has begun her first Level Three Mela in 2019.

MutShat practices a Kemetic spiritual system and is a healer *wabet* (priestess), and *seba* (teacher) of Ankh Kemetic Energy Medicine, an ancient technology akin to reiki (she was attuned by Ra Sekhi founder Rekhit Kajara Nia Yaa Nebthet). She is level one certified in foot reflexology and in sacred art and yoga. As a community wellness advocate, MutShat is available for teaching, wellness, and speaking engagements. You may contact her at inlightyoga108@gmail.com or find out more about her at www.purestlightwellness.love. Sat Nam, Wahe Guru!

KRI PUBLICATIONS

A Kundalini Yoga Global Community
KUNDALINIRESEARCHINSTITUTE.ORG

Milton Keynes UK
Ingram Content Group UK Ltd.
UKHW051136161023
430683UK00005B/22

9 780978 69894